Contents

Differentiation of topics for 3 levels of ability

To differentiate the learning activities, the games have been colour coded according to the amount of Italian words that appear in the games. "verde" is for the lower ability group, "giallo" is for the middle ability group, and "rosso" is for the higher ability group.

	verde	giallo	rosso
Drinks	una coca-cola una limonata un'acqua un succo	una coca-cola una limonata un'acqua minerale un succo d'arancia un tè un caffè	una coca-cola una limonata un'acqua minerale un succo d'arancia una coca-cola light una cioccolata un tè un caffè un latte
Numbers	uno due tre quattro cinque sei	uno due tre quattro cinque sei sette otto nove dieci	uno due tre quattro cinque sei sette otto nove dieci undici dodici
Fruit	la mela la banana il kiwi il melone	la mela la banana il kiwi il melone la fragola l'arancia	la mela la bana[illegible] il ki[illegible] il [illegible]
Pet animals	un gatto un cane un pesce un serpente	un gatto un cane un pesce un serpente un coniglio un cavallo	un gatto un cane un pesce un serpente un coniglio un cavallo un uccello una tartaruga un topo
Colours	rosso blu verde giallo	rosso blu verde giallo marrone rosa bianco nero	rosso blu verde giallo marrone rosa bianco nero porpora grigio arancione grigio argento
Sport	il calcio il tennis il mini-golf il ping-pong	il tennis il mini-golf il ping-pong la pallacanestro il calcio il nuoto	il tennis il mini-golf il ping-pong la pallacanestro il calcio il nuoto il volano il rugby
Transport	il treno il pullman la nave la macchina	il treno il pullman la nave la macchina la bicicletta l'aereo	il treno il pullman la nave la macchina la bicicletta l'aereo la moto la barca il razzo
Pizzas & Pizza toppings	il formaggio i funghi i peperoni i pomodori	il formaggio i funghi i peperoni i pomodori il prosciutto le cipolle	il formaggio i funghi i peperoni i pomodori il prosciutto le cipolle il salame la mozzarella l'ananas

Teachers note: You could ask the pupils to match the picture mini card to the correct word card. See page 75 for pair work activities using the mini cards, and page 77 for class activities.

Teachers note: Photocopy this page (on card if possible), then make 8 cards by cutting round the cards. If you use card of **3 or 4 different colours** it is easier to separate the sets when handing them out to the class.

Can I say 4 drinks in Italian?

Start at "Comincia quì", roll the dice and count that number of spaces.
Say the drink you land on in Italian. To win, arrive first at "Hai vinto!"

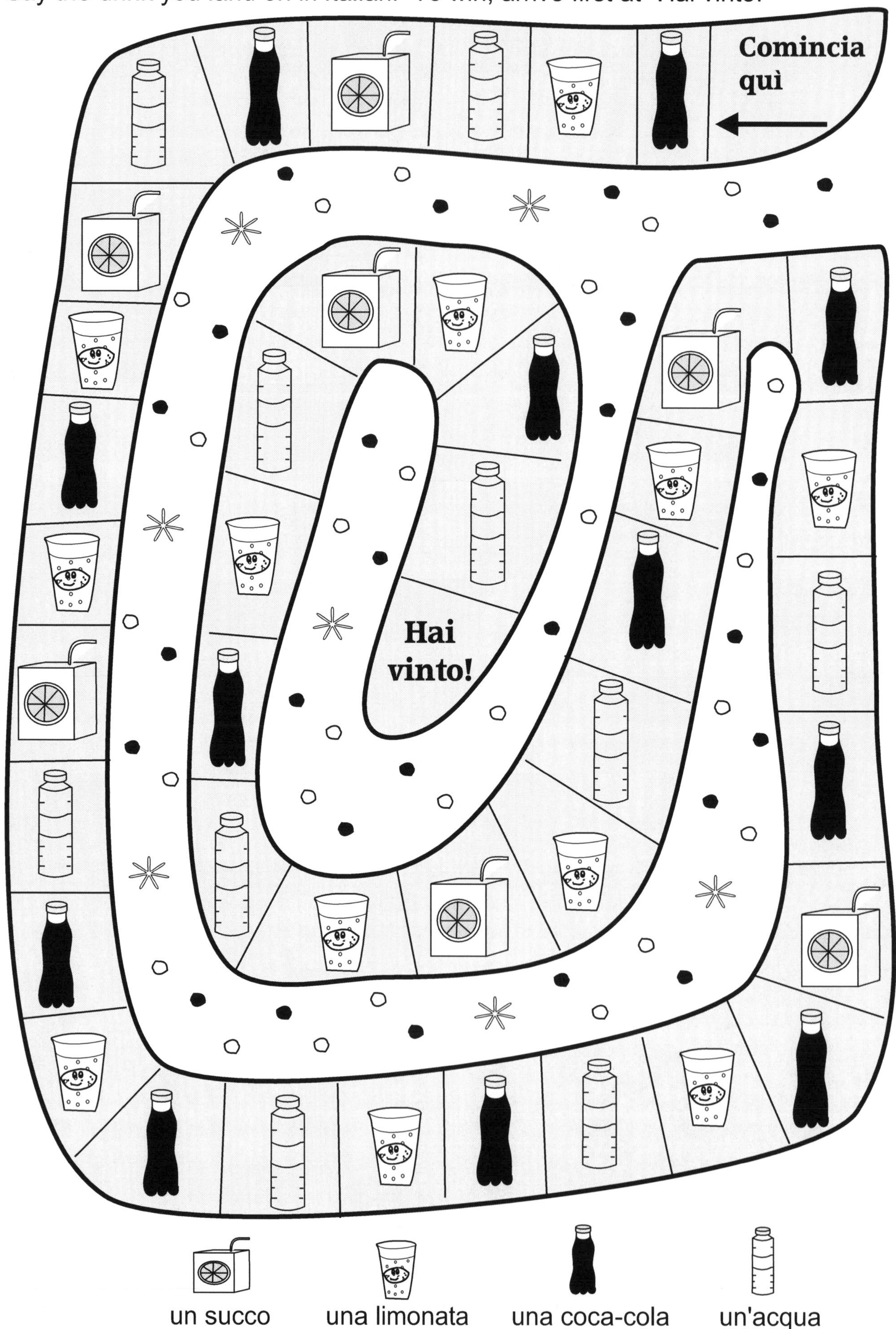

un succo | una limonata | una coca-cola | un'acqua

Can I say 4 drinks in Italian?

For this game, each person will need 8 domino cards. To make eight domino cards, with an adult cut along the dotted lines. Then, take turns to put a card down by matching a word to a picture or vice versa. If you cannot match a card, miss a turn. The winner is the person to either use all their cards, or use as many cards as possible.

Can I say six drinks in Italian?

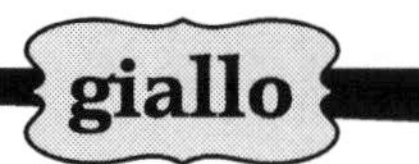

Start at “Comincia quì”, roll the dice and count that number of spaces.
Say the drink you land on in Italian. To win, arrive first at “Hai vinto!”

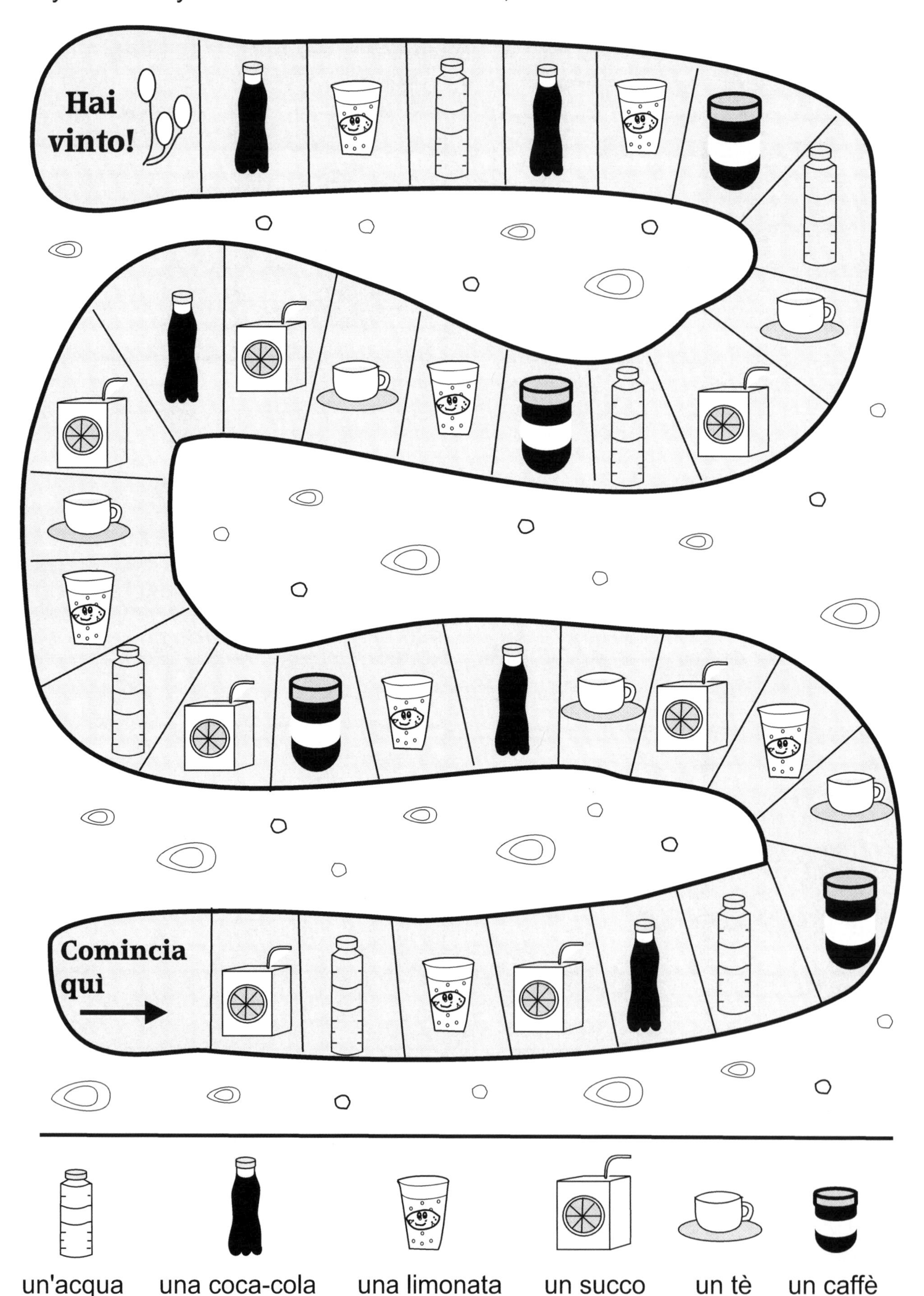

Can I say six drinks in Italian?

Each person / team needs 5 coloured counters or cubes of one colour (or a set of noughts or a set of crosses). Say the Italian word for the drink or essential word as you cover it with your counter.
To win you have to get 3 in a row (vertically, horizontally or diagonally).

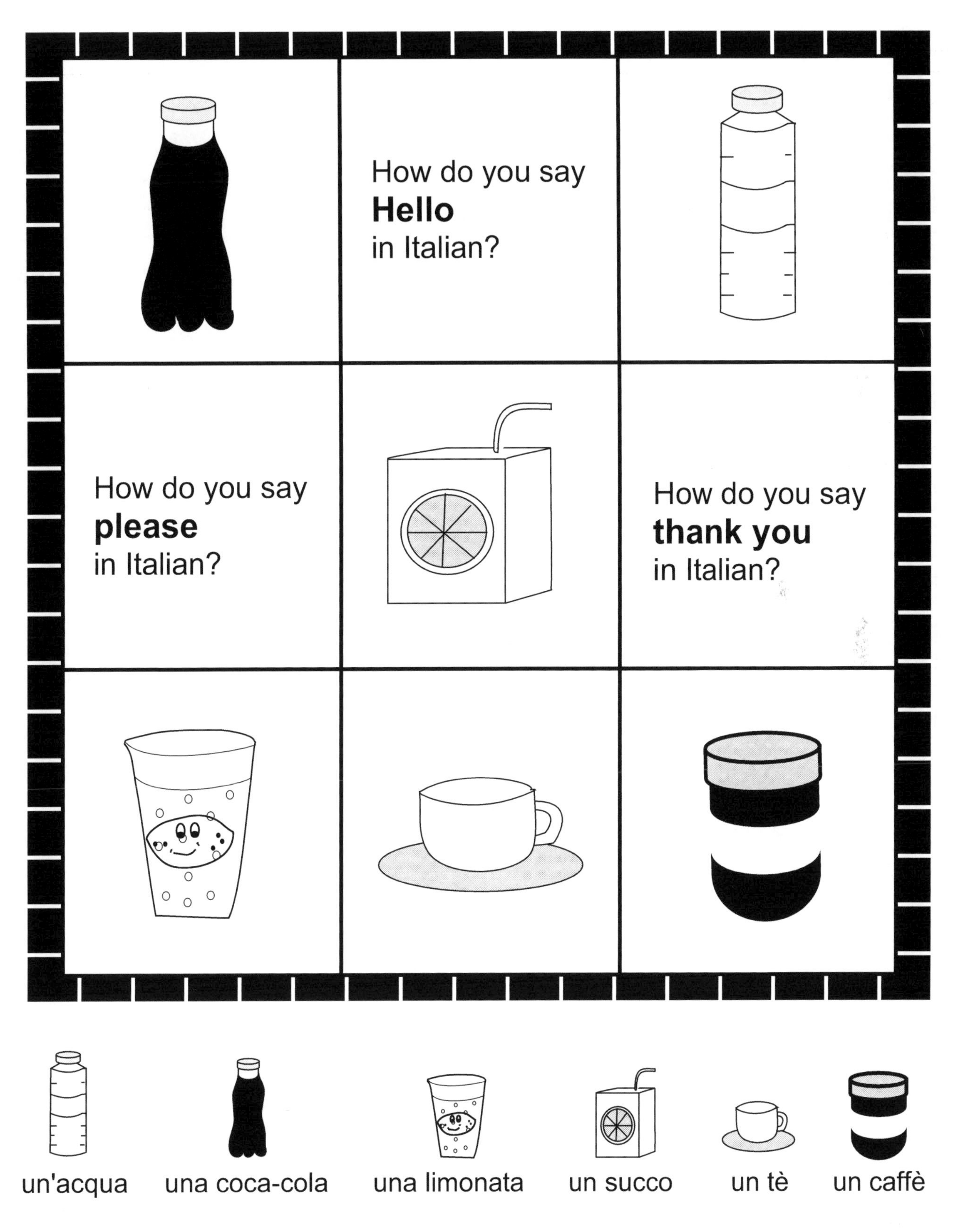

un'acqua   una coca-cola   una limonata   un succo   un tè   un caffè

Ciao = Hello   per favore = please   grazie = thank you

Can I say 9 drinks in Italian?

Start at "Comincia quì", roll the dice and count that number of squares.
Say the drink you land on in Italian. To win, arrive first at "Hai vinto!"

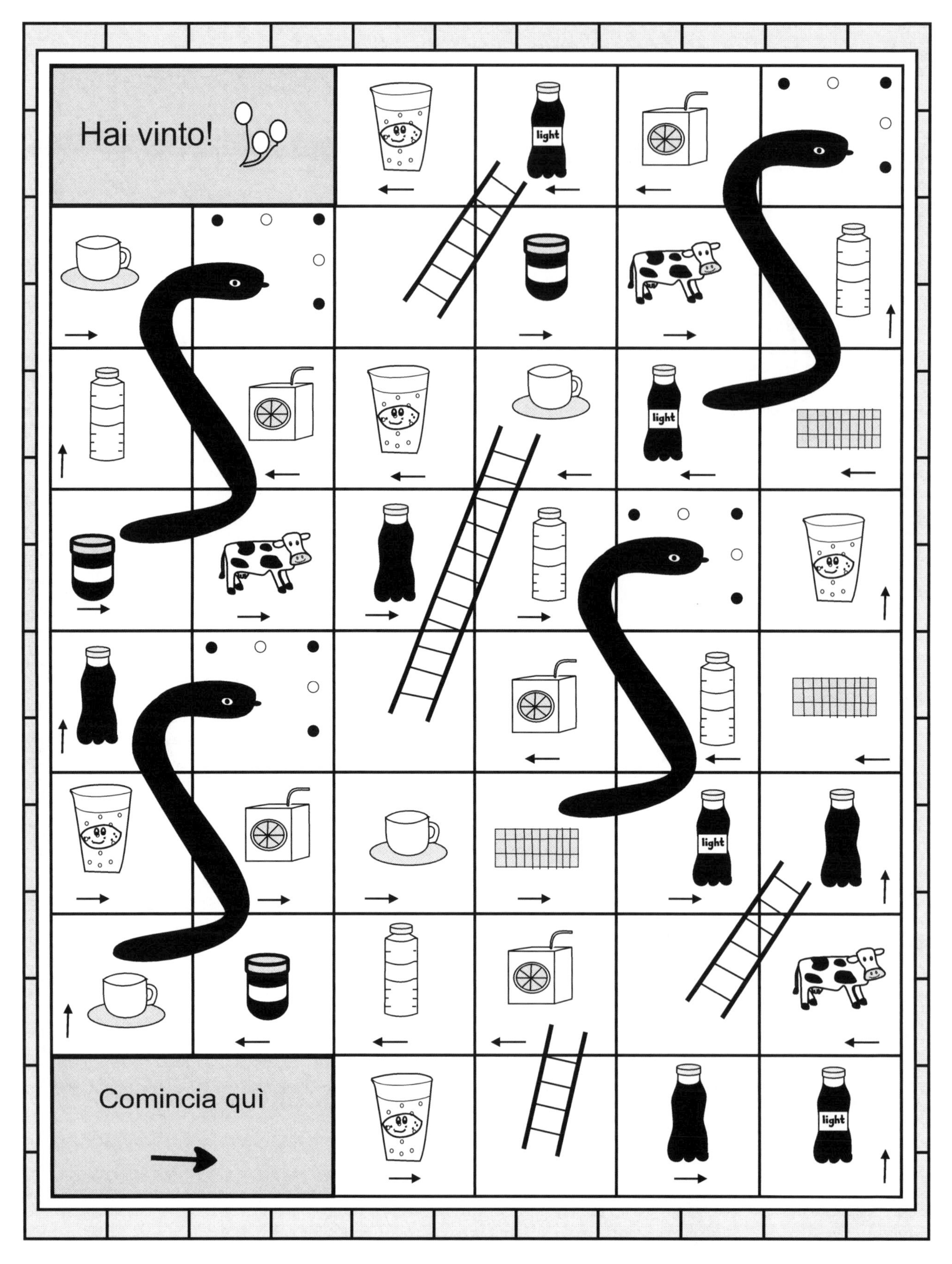

un'acqua   una coca-cola   una limonata   una coca-cola light

un succo   un tè   un caffè   una cioccolata   un latte

Can I say 9 drinks in Italian?

rosso

Each person / team needs 5 coloured counters or cubes of one colour (or a set of noughts or a set of crosses). Say the Italian word for the drink as you cover it with your counter. To win you have to get 3 in a row (vertically, horizontally or diagonally).

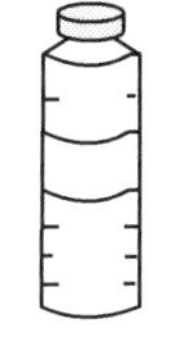
un'acqua

una coca-cola

una limonata

un succo

una coca-cola light

un tè

un caffè

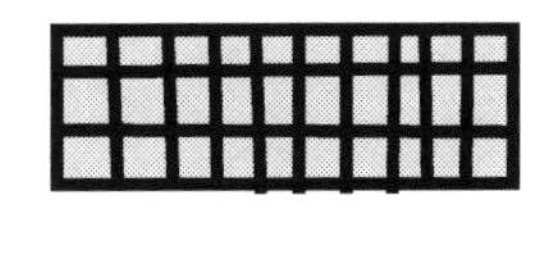
una cioccolata

un latte

Making sentences with drinks

When the pupils play the games, they could either practise just the vocabulary for the topic, or they could say a whole sentence. The pupils could write the phrase being practised on a mini whiteboard in front of them, or you could write the phrase on the whiteboard in the classroom.

Here are some ideas of the sentences you could instruct a group, or the whole class to practise for the drinks topic:

1) **Asking for a drink: Vorrei .... per favore** (I would like ....please)
e.g. Vorrei un succo d'arancia, per favore.
Or say the drink, and then per favore after it e.g. una coca-cola, per favore

2) **Saying what you are drinking**:
Bevo (I am drinking) e.g. Bevo una limonata.

3) **Giving opinions or preferences about drinks:**

Mi piace = I like	Mi piace l'acqua
Non mi piace = I don't like	Non mi piace il tè
Preferisco = I prefer	Preferisco la coca-cola light

Tell the pupils that when they say what drinks they like, dislike or prefer they need to use either il / l' / la / lo (the) instead of the un / una (a).

4) **Asking what drink friends like:** Ti piace..........? (Do you like.......?)
e.g. Ti piace il caffè?

5) **Saying what is healthy to drink:**
Fa bene alla salute bere ...... (It's good for your health to drink.....)
E.g. Fa bene alla salute bere l'acqua minerale

Fa male alla salute bere ....(It's bad for your health to drink......)
e.g. Fa male alla salute bere la coca-cola.

6) **Saying there isn't certain drinks** (as unfortunately sometimes cafés run out or may not sell what you want).
Non c'è ..... (There isn't) e.g. Non c'è la coca-cola light.

Teachers note: You could ask the pupils to match the picture mini card to the correct word card. See page 75 for pair work activities using the mini cards, and page 77 for class activities.

Teachers note: Photocopy this page (on card if possible), then make 8 cards by cutting round the cards. If you use card of **3 or 4 different colours** it is easier to separate the sets when handing them out to the class.

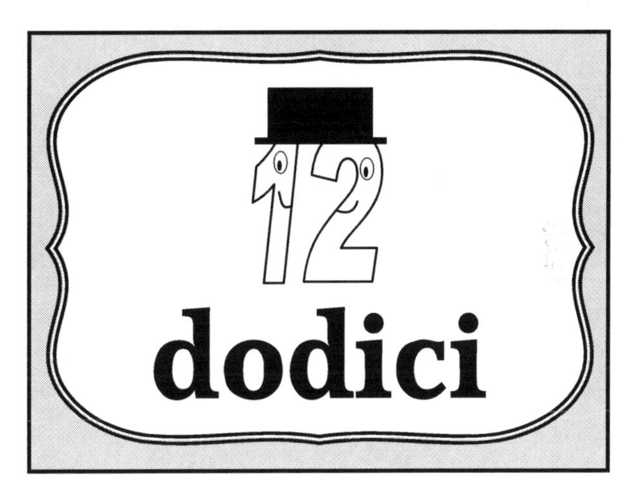

Making sentences with numbers

1) **Asking for quantities of things:** Explain to the pupils that if they wanted to ask for a particular quantity of something in a shop they would have to say the number of items they wanted, and add **per favore** (please) at the end. Ask the pupils to say the numbers that appear in the games followed by per favore. e.g. due, per favore.

2) **Saying how old you are**: Teach the phrase **Ho .....anni** (I am ..... years old) Ask the pupils to play the number games, but rather than just say the number say the corresponding age for each number they have in the games. If they get the number 1 it would be Ho un anno.

3) **Saying different quantities of things:** Choose a noun for the pupils to practise, For example un gelato (an ice cream). When using the word “gelato” if they land on 1, they say “un gelato”, If they land on 2 they say “due gelati” for 3 “tre gelati” etc

Can I say 6 numbers in Italian? verde

Start at “Comincia quì”, roll the dice and count that number of spaces.
Say the number you land on in Italian. To win, arrive first at “Hai vinto!”

Hai vinto! 5 3 1 4 2
5
1 3 6 4 3 6
5 4 5
4 2 3 2 4
2 1 5
6 5 2 6 3 1
5
3 4 1 5 6 1 4
5
Comincia quì → 5 2 3 2 6

1 = uno 2 = due 3 = tre 4 = quattro 5 = cinque 6 = sei

The ten points game

Take turns to roll a dice. If you can say the number you have thrown in Italian you get a point. If you roll the number six, and say the number six in Italian you get two points. Who will be the first person to get ten points?

Can I say 9 numbers in Italian?

Each person / team needs 5 coloured counters or cubes of one colour (or a set of noughts or a set of crosses).

Say the Italian word for the number as you cover it with your counter. To win you have to get 3 in a row (vertically, horizontally or diagonally).

1	2	3	4	5	6	7	8	9
uno	**due**	**tre**	**quattro**	**cinque**	**sei**	**sette**	**otto**	**nove**

Can I say 10 numbers in Italian?

Start at "Comincia quì", roll the dice and count that number of squares. If the final square has the bottom of the ladder in it go up it, or if it has the head of a snake go down it. Say the number of the square you land on in Italian. Take turns to roll the dice. To win, arrive first at "Hai vinto!"

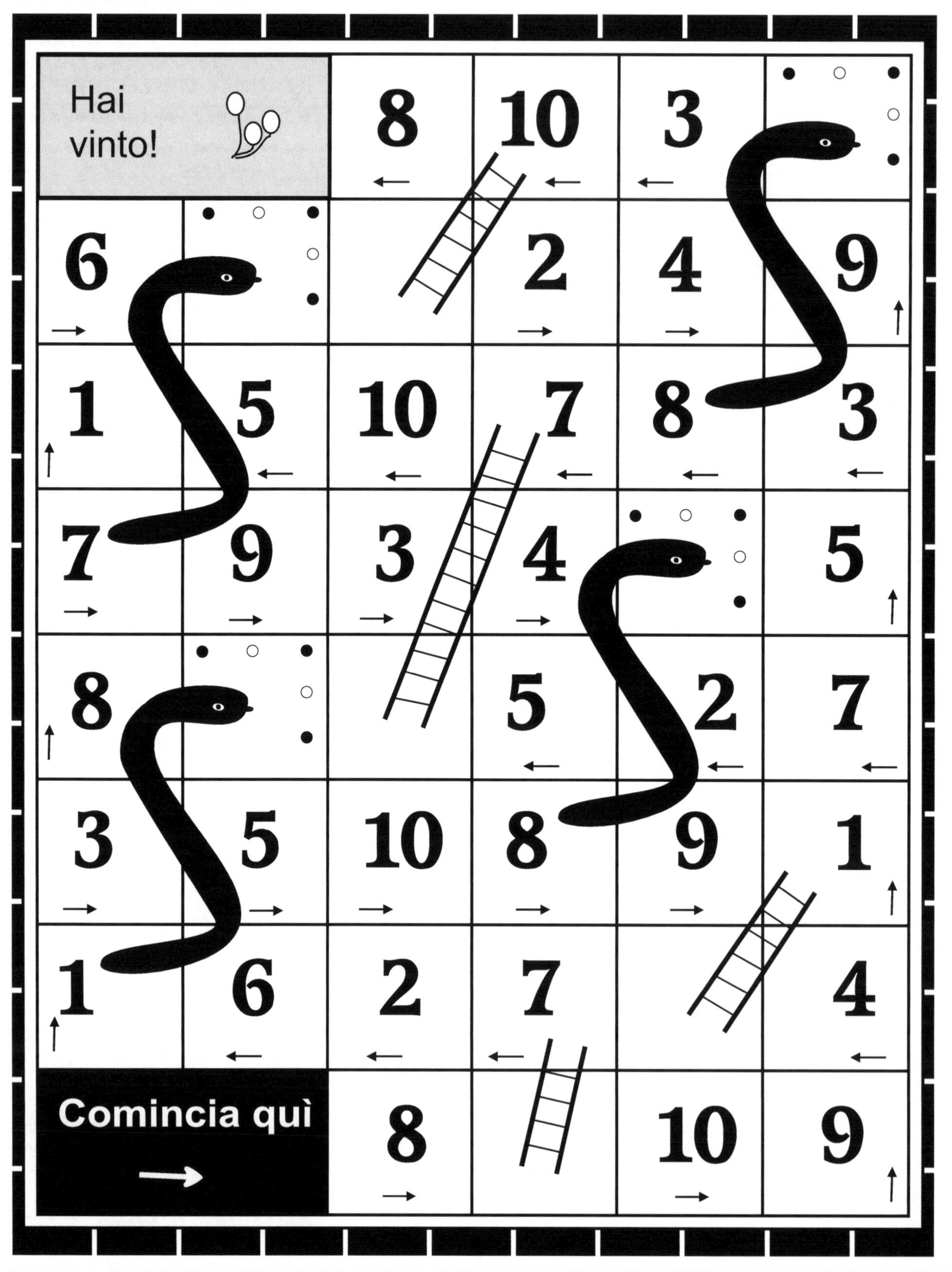

1	2	3	4	5	6	7	8	9	10
uno	due	tre	quattro	cinque	sei	sette	otto	nove	dieci

Can I say 12 numbers in Italian? 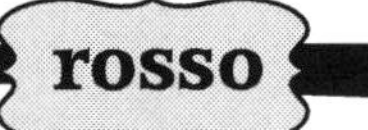

Start at "Comincia quì", roll the dice and count that number of spaces.
Say the number you land on in Italian. To win, arrive first at "Hai vinto!"

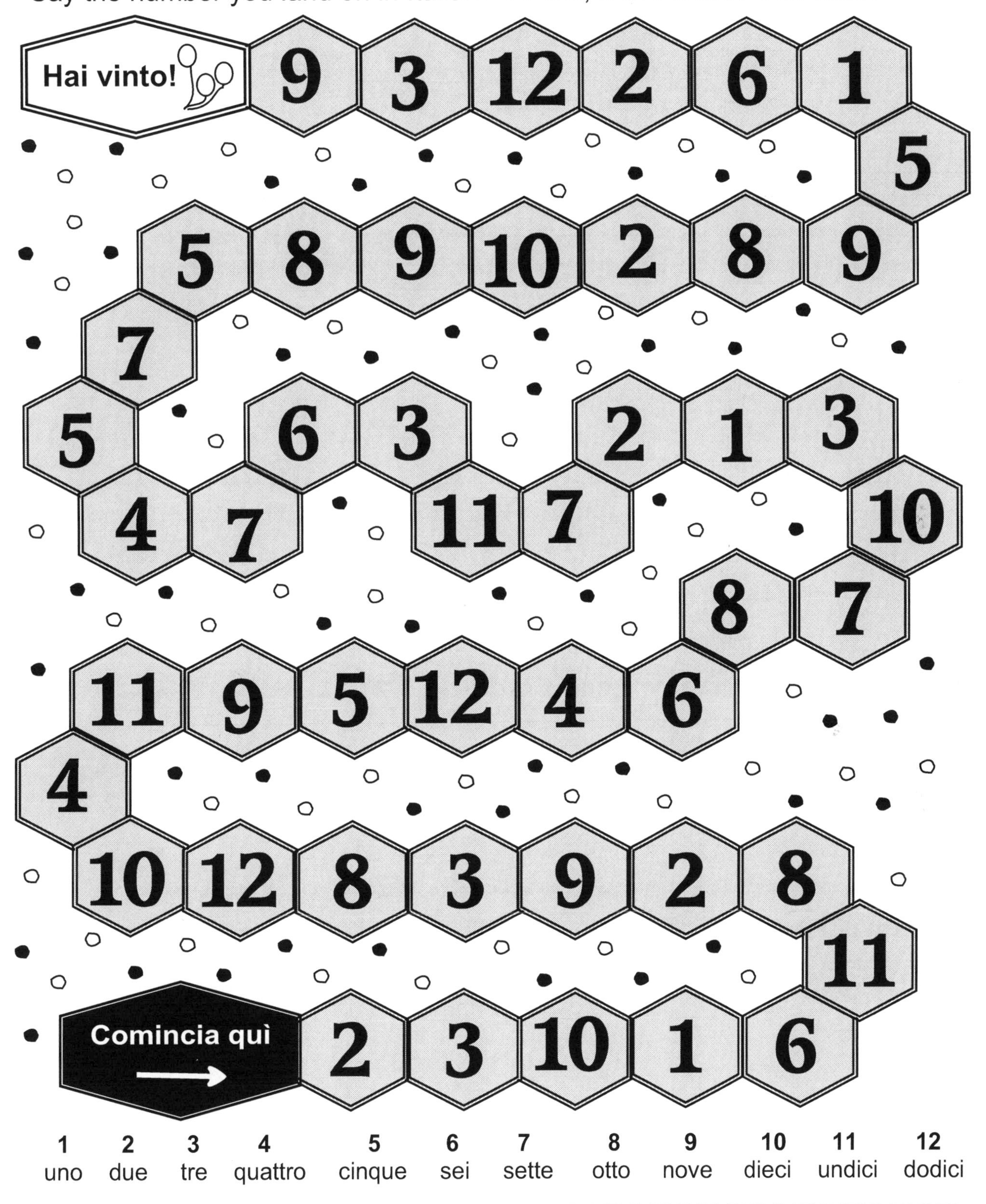

1	2	3	4	5	6	7	8	9	10	11	12
uno	due	tre	quattro	cinque	sei	sette	otto	nove	dieci	undici	dodici

The ten points game

Take turns to roll TWO dice. If you can say the number you have thrown in Italian you get a point. If you roll the number six, and say the number six in Italian you get two points. If you roll the number twelve, and say this number in Italian you get three points. Who will be the first person to get ten points?

Teachers note: Ask the pupils to match the picture mini card to the correct word card.
See page 75 for pair work activities using the mini cards, and page 77 for class activities.

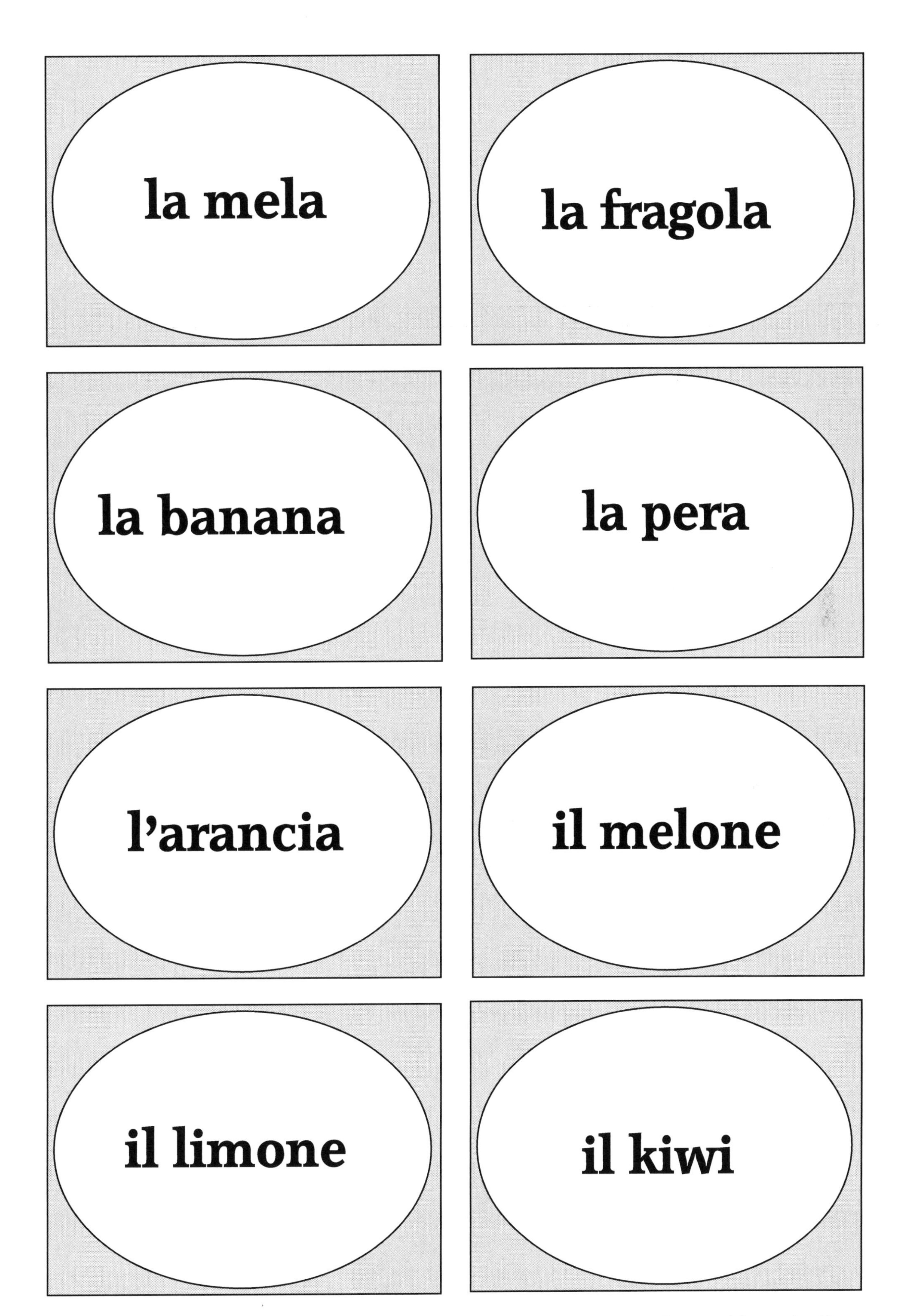

Teachers note: Photocopy this page (on card if possible), then make 8 cards by cutting round the cards. If you use card of **3 or 4 different colours** it is easier to separate the sets when handing them out to the class.

Can I say 4 fruit in Italian?

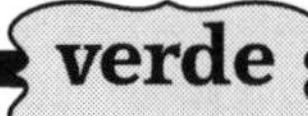

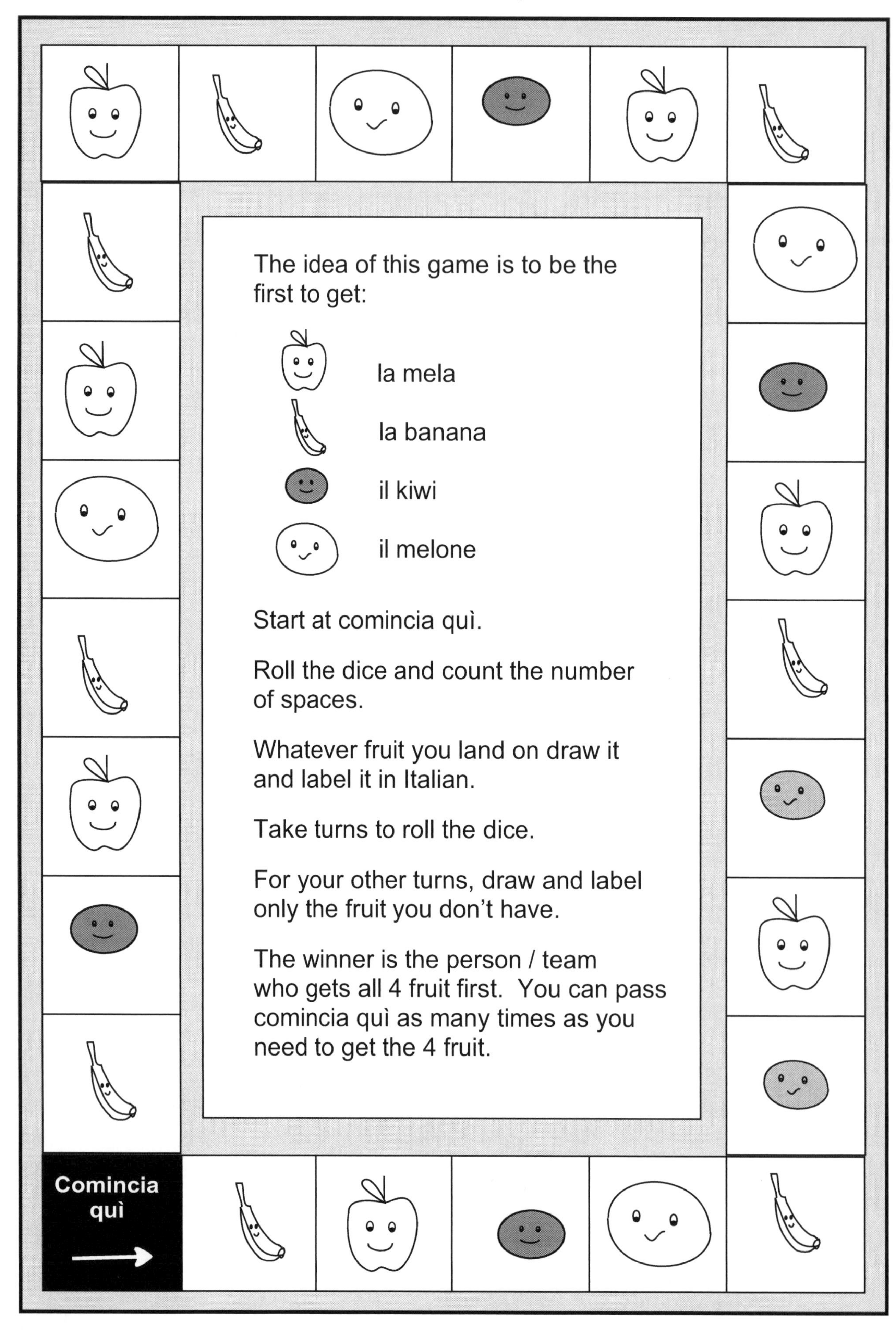

Can I say 4 fruit in Italian?

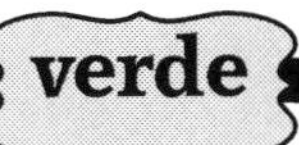

Roll two dice and find the coordinate by counting along the bottom for the first dice, and up the side for the second dice. Say the fruit in Italian for the coordinate to get a point, e.g 4,3 = la mela. The winner Is the person or team who gets the most points.

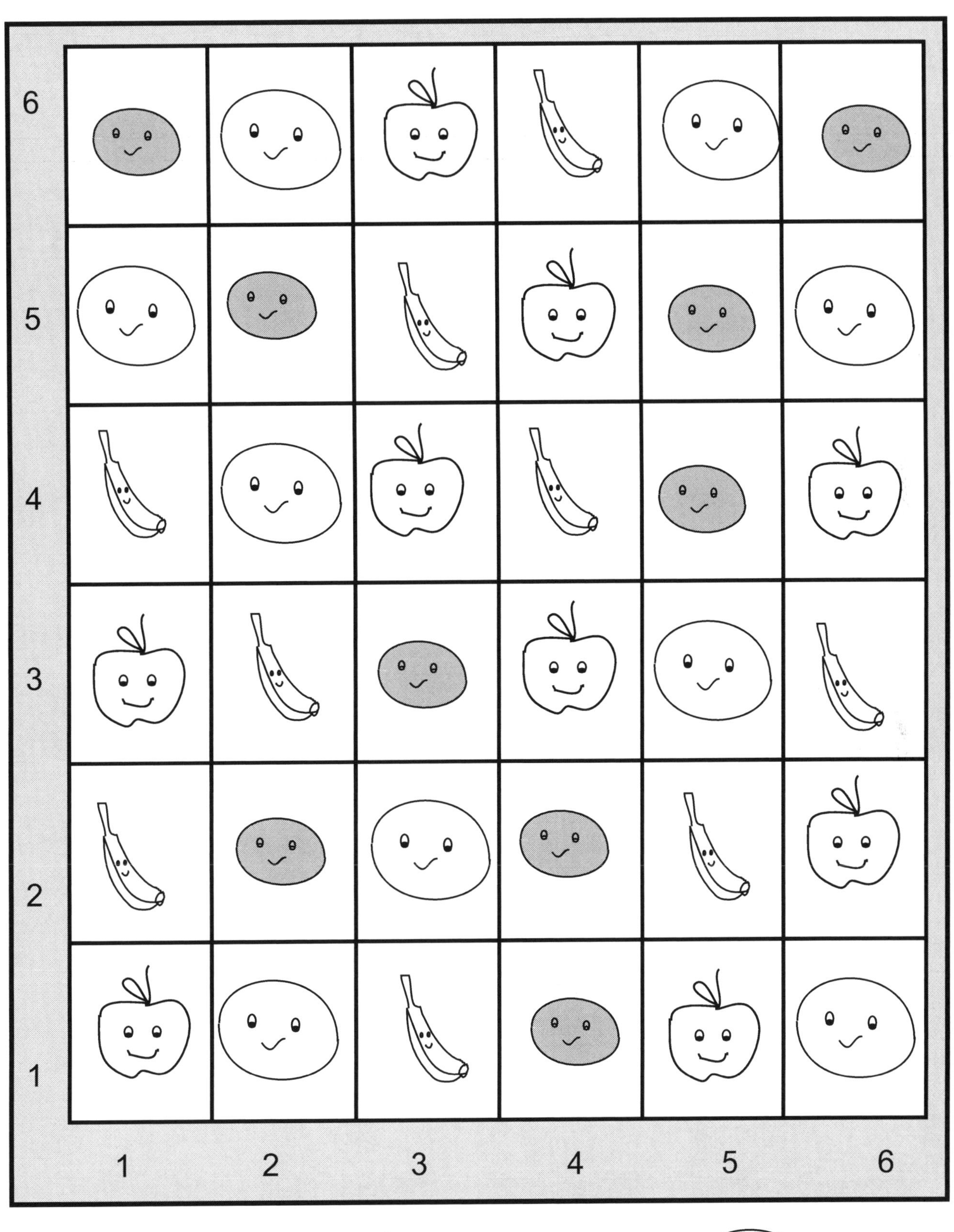

la mela

la banana

il kiwi

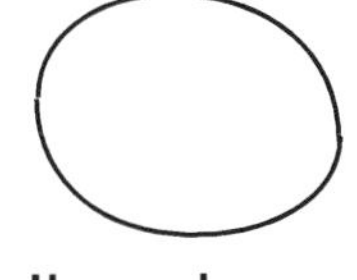

il melone

Can I say 6 fruits in Italian?

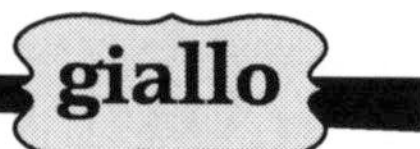

Start at comincia quì, roll the dice and count that number of spaces. Say the fruit you land on in Italian. Take turns to roll the dice. To win, arrive first at hai vinto.

la mela | la banana | il kiwi | il melone | la fragola | l'arancia

Can I say 6 fruits in Italian?

Each person / team needs 5 coloured counters or cubes of one colour (or a set of noughts or a set of crosses). Say the Italian word for the fruit or number as you place your counter on it. To win you have to get 3 in a row (vertically, horizontally or diagonally).

1 = uno 2 = due 3 = tre

la mela

la banana

il kiwi

il melone

la fragola

l'arancia

Can I say 8 fruits in Italian?

Start at comincia quì, roll the dice and count that number of squares. If the final square has the bottom of the ladder in it go up it, or if it has the head of a snake go down it. Say the fruit you land on in Italian. Take turns to roll the dice. To win, arrive first at hai vinto.

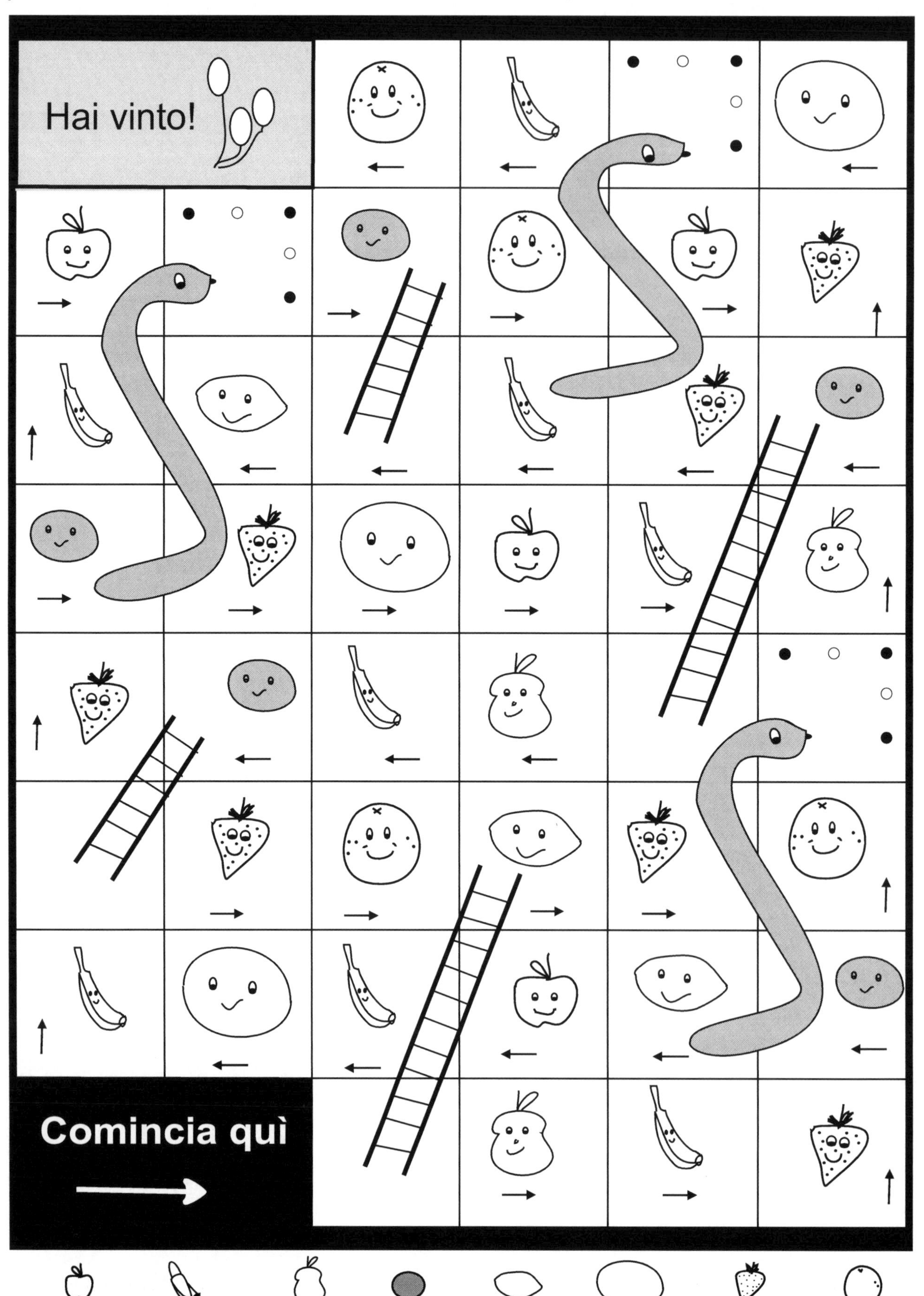

la mela | la banana | la pera | il kiwi | il limone | il melone | la fragola | l'arancia

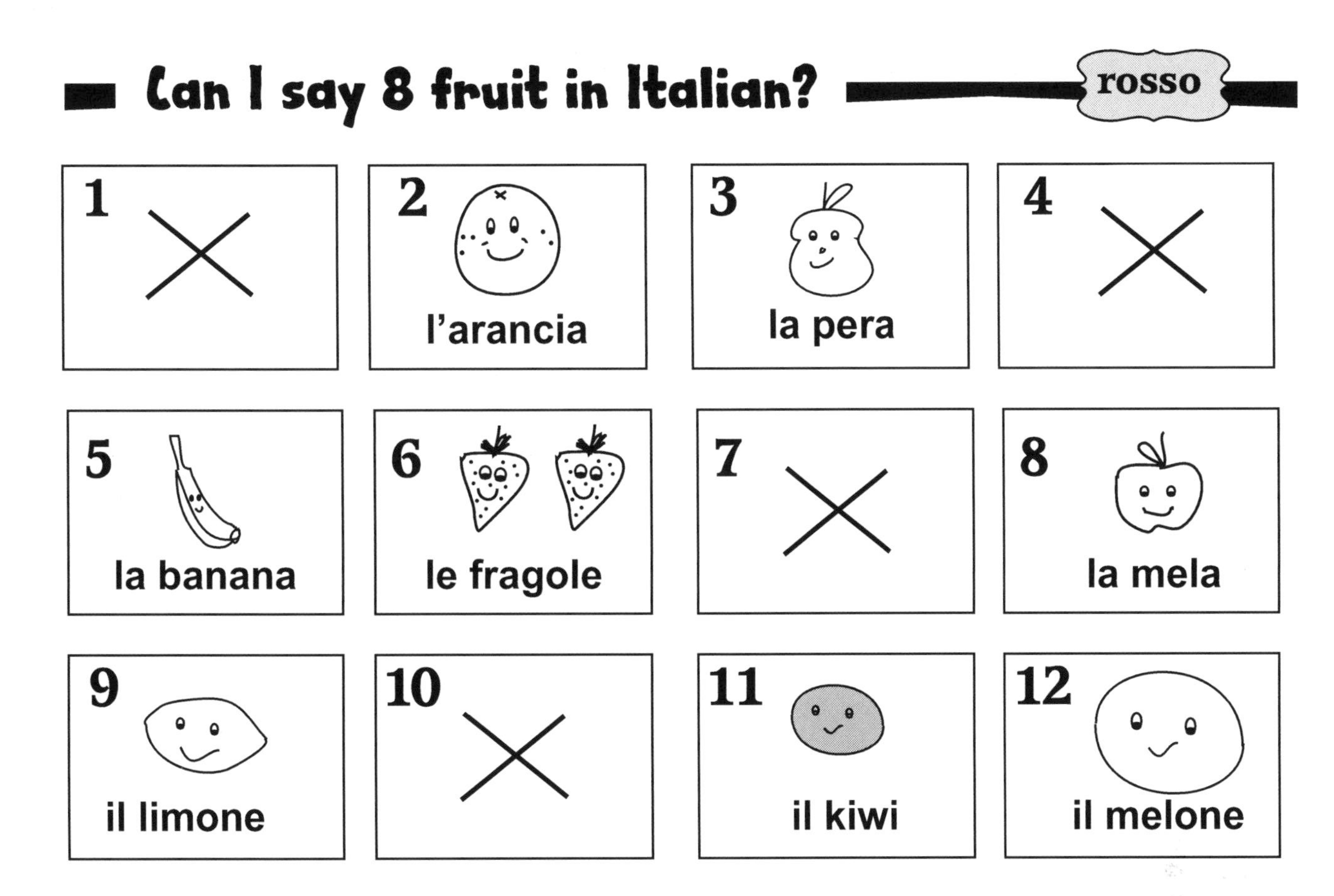

Roll two dice, and add the numbers together. Look at the above numbers, if there is a fruit for the number you get, say what the fruit is in Italian and win a point. If you get **le fragole** you get two points! Who will be the first to ten points?

Making sentences with fruit

When the pupils play the games, they could either practise just the vocabulary for the topic, or they could say a whole sentence. Here are some ideas of the sentences you could instruct a group, or the whole class to practise for the fruit topic:

1) **Giving opinions or preferences about fruit.** In the word list section the fruit also appear in the plural form. This list can be photocopied and given to the pupils for when they are talking about which fruit they like.

Mi piacciono = I like e.g. Mi piacciono le fragole

Non mi piacciono = I don't like e.g. Non mi piacciono le banane

2) **Asking what fruit friends like**. **Ti piacciono ...?** (Do you like.......?)
e.g. Ti piacciono le arance?

3) **Using the correct word order for colours and nouns**: explain to the pupils that colours go after nouns in Italian and that some colours have an **a** added at the end of the word instead of the o when the nouns are feminine and in the singular form.
e.g. la banana gialla, la mela verde, la fragola rossa .....

4) **Going to the market: Un chilo di ....., per favore** (A kilo of ..... please)
Tell the pupils that if they went shopping they would usually ask for the fruit as a weight in kilos. After un chilo di you need to say the fruit in the plural, but without the word le or i (the), e.g. Un chilo di mele.

Teachers note: see page 75 for pair work activities using the mini cards, and page 77 for class activities using the mini cards.

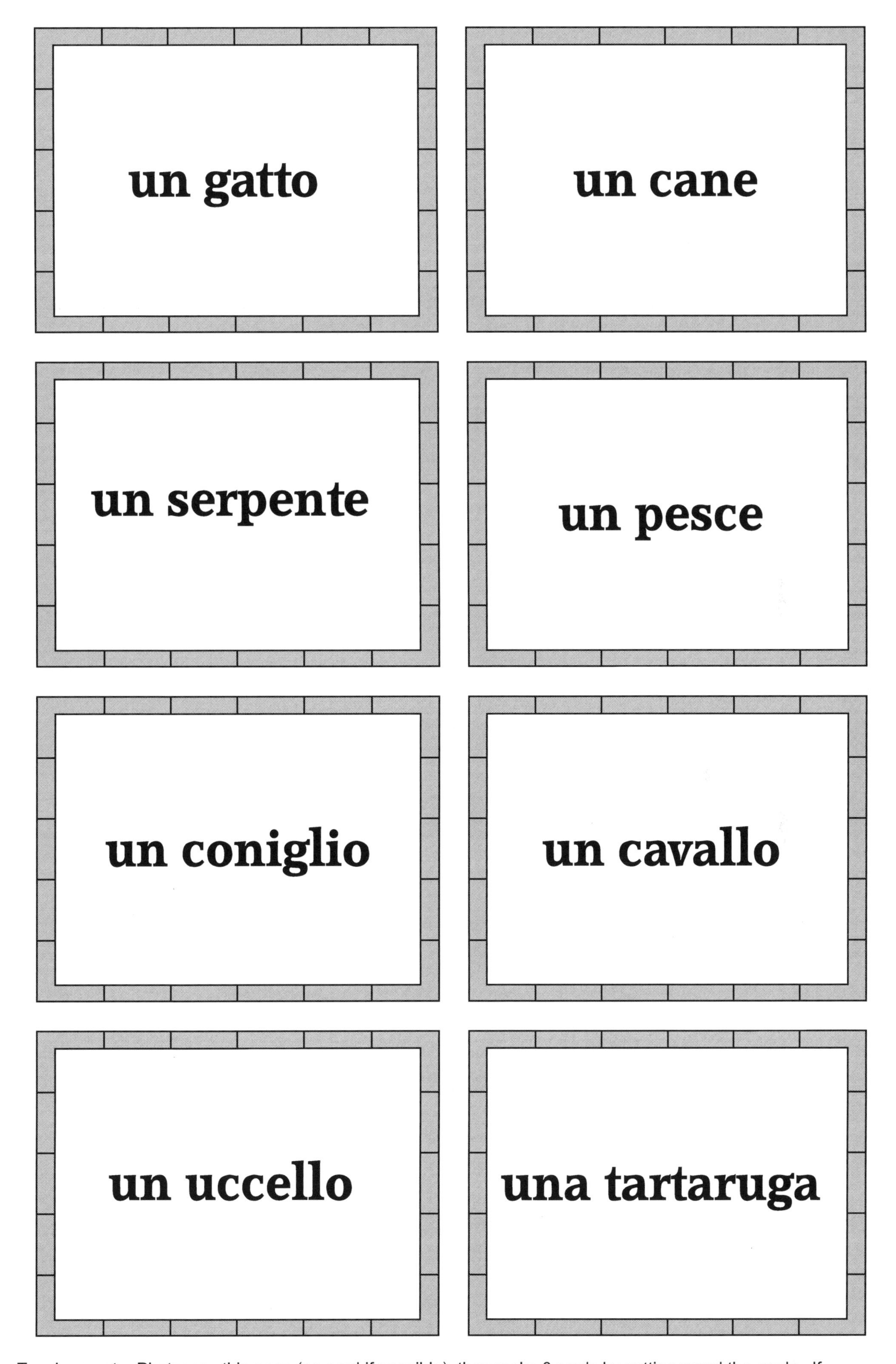

Teachers note: Photocopy this page (on card if possible), then make 8 cards by cutting round the cards. If you use card of **3 or 4 different colours** it is easier to separate the sets when handing them out to the class.

Can I say 4 animals in Italian?

verde

Start at "Comincia quì", roll the dice and count that number of spaces.
Say the animal you land on in Italian. To win, arrive first at "Hai vinto!"

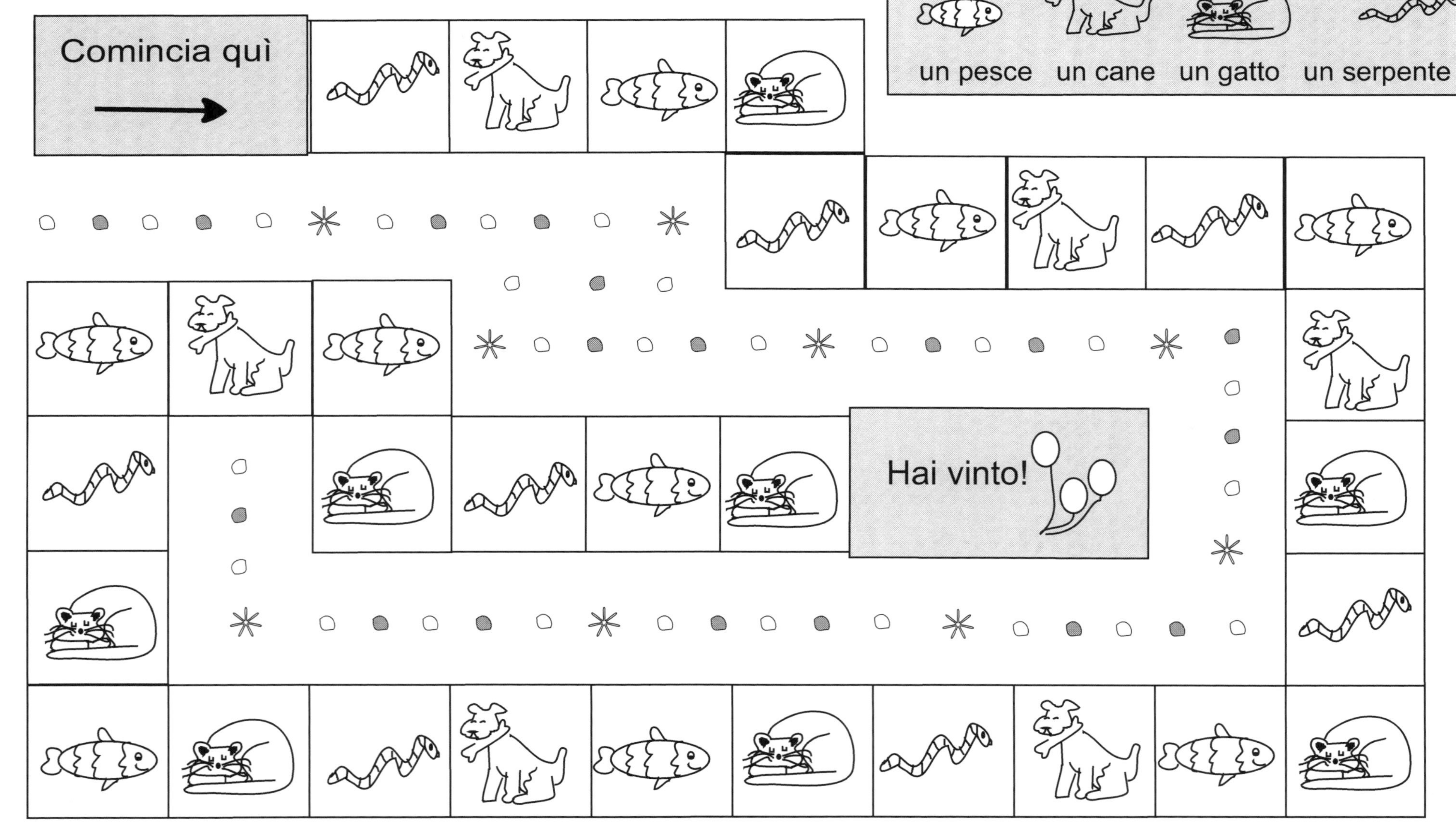

Can I say 4 animals & 1 to 5 in Italian?

Each person / team needs 5 coloured counters or cubes of one colour (or a set of noughts or a set of crosses).
Say the Italian word for the animal or number as you place your counter.
To win you have to get 3 in a row (vertically, horizontally or diagonally).

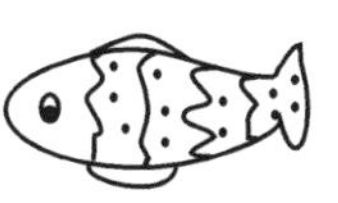
un pesce

un cane

un gatto

un serpente

1 = uno   2 = due   3 = tre   4 = quattro   5 = cinque

Can I say 6 animals in Italian?

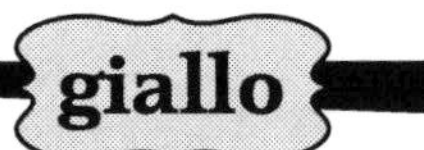

Start at "Comincia quì", roll the dice and count that number of spaces. Say the animal you land on in Italian. To win, arrive first at "Hai vinto!"

un coniglio

un cavallo

un pesce

un cane

un gatto

un serpente

Can I say 6 animals in Italian?

Roll two dice and find the **coordinate** by counting along the bottom for the first dice, and up the side for the second dice. Say the animal in Italian for the coordinate to get a point, e.g. 3, 2 = un gatto. The winner is the person or team who gets the most points.

un coniglio

un cavallo

un pesce

un cane

un gatto

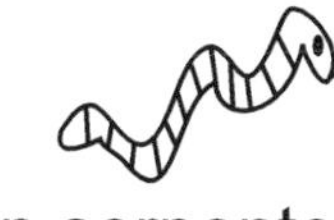
un serpente

Can I say 9 animals in Italian?

Each person / team needs 15 coloured counters or cubes of one colour.

Say the Italian word for the animal as you place your counter or cube.
To win you have to get 4 in a row (vertically, horizontally or diagonally).

un coniglio

un cavallo

un pesce

un cane

un gatto

un serpente

un uccello

un topo

una tartaruga

Can I say 9 animals in Italian? - Pupil A rosso

Each pupil cuts out a set of **dominoes** by cutting along the dotted lines. Take turns to put a card down by matching a word to a picture or vice versa. If you cannot match a card, miss a turn. The winner is the person to either use all their cards, or use as many cards as possible.

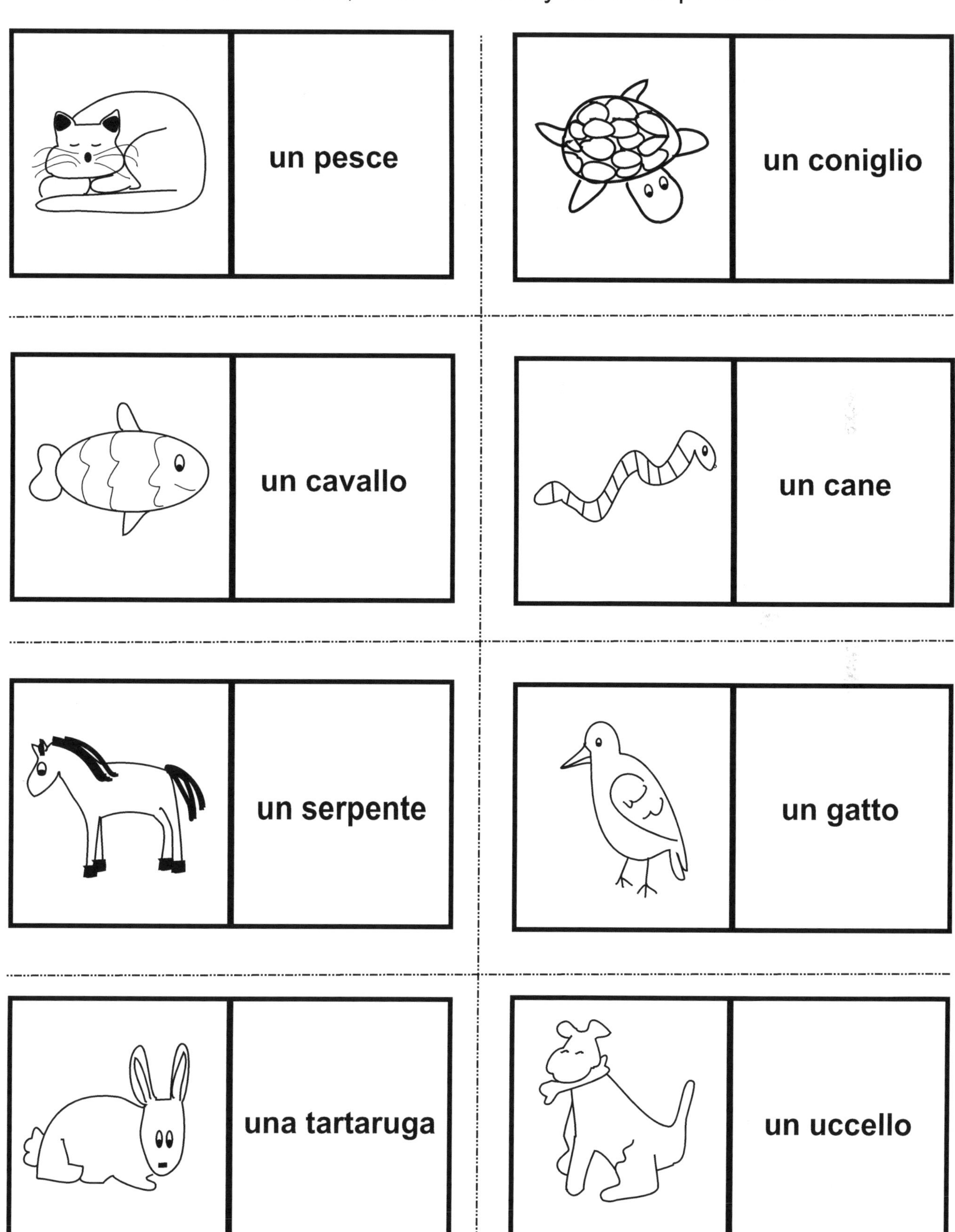

Can I say 9 animals in Italian? - Pupil B

Each pupil cuts out a set of **dominoes** by cutting along the dotted lines. Take turns to put a card down by matching a word to a picture or vice versa. If you cannot match a card, miss a turn. The winner is the person to either use all their cards, or use as many cards as possible.

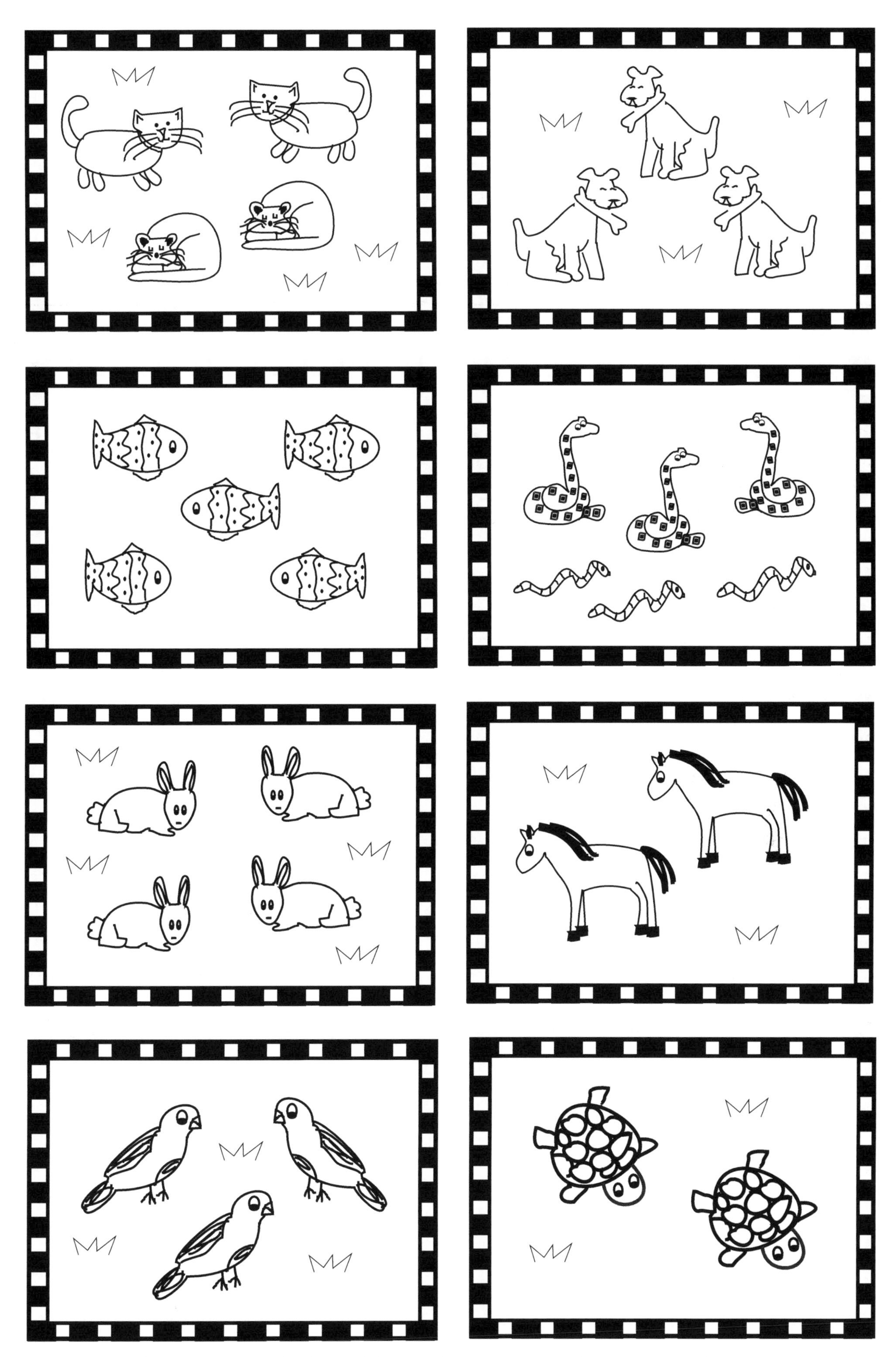

Teachers note: Ask the pupils to match the picture mini card to the correct word card.
See page 75 for pair work activities using the mini cards, and page 77 for class activities.

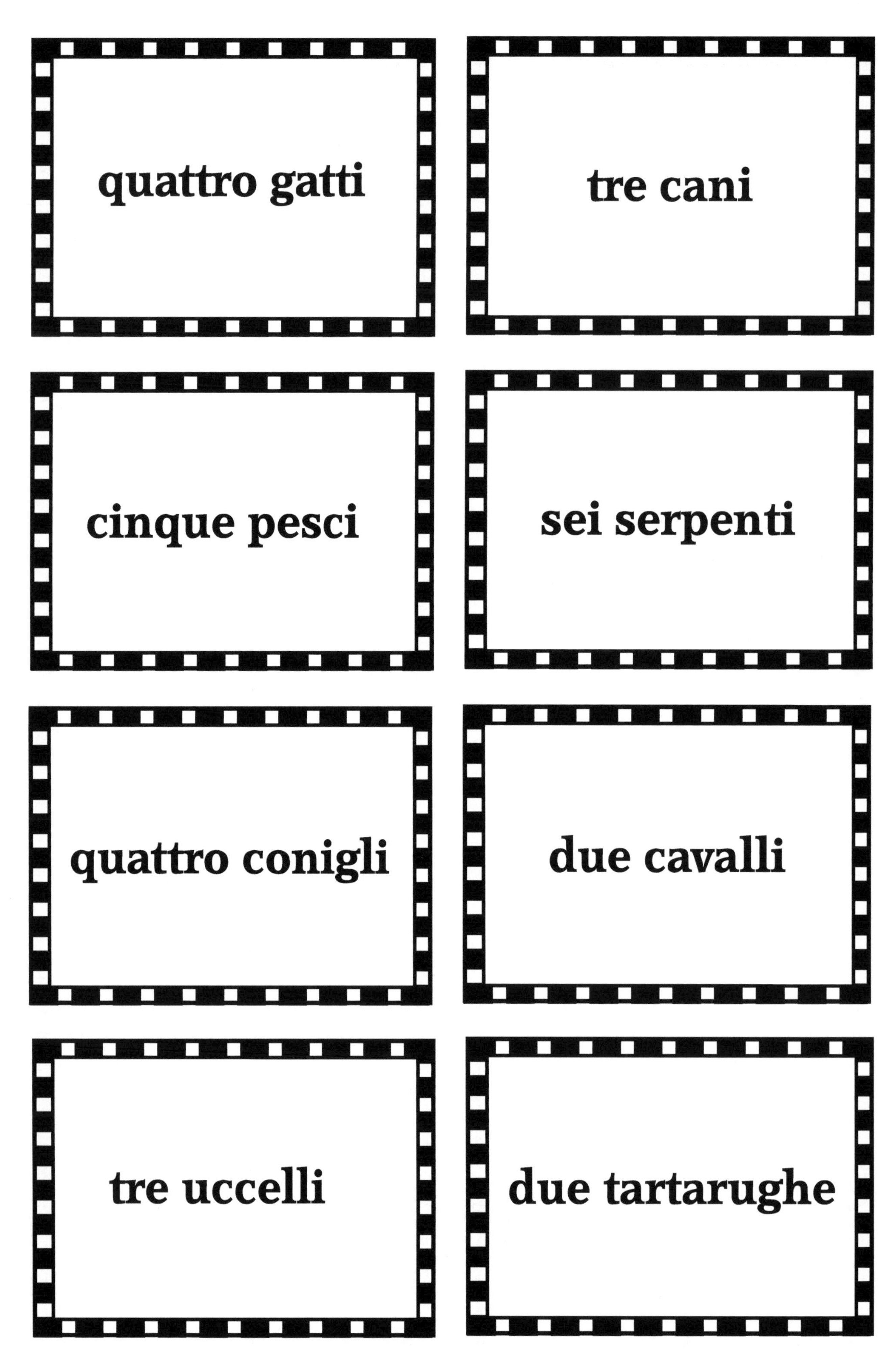

Teachers note: Photocopy this page (on card if possible), then make 8 cards by cutting round the cards. If you use card of **3 or 4 different colours** it is easier to separate the sets when handing them out to the class.

Making sentences with pet animals

When the pupils play the games, they could either practise just the vocabulary for the topic, or they could say a whole sentence. Here are some ideas of the sentences you could instruct a group, or the whole class to practise for the pet animals topic:

1) **Saying if you have a pet**: Ho = I have e.g. Ho un gatto.

2) **Asking a friend if they have a particular animal:** Hai .....? (Do you have...?) e.g. Hai un cane? Hai un coniglio?

3) **Describing the colour of the animals:** Ask the pupils to invent a colour for each of the pets, and say the colour after the Italian word for the animal. The games can be coloured in by the pupils. e.g. un cane marrone, un coniglio grigio

4) **Is it big or small?**: Ask the pupils to decide if the animal is big or small, and say either grande (big) or piccolo (small) after the Italian word for the animal. e.g. un gatto grande

5) **Saying if you would like a particular animal**:

Vorrei....(I would like .....) e.g. Vorrei un uccello. Vorrei un cavallo.

Non vorrei .... (I wouldn't like...) e.g. Non vorrei un serpente.

6) **Saying that you used to have a particular animal:** Avevo ... (I used to have...) e.g. Avevo un pesce. Avevo una tartaruga.

7) **Talking about which pets you like**: Tell the pupils that for saying if they like a particular animal they need to say the Italian for "I like" in the plural and also the type of animal they like. There is a photocopiable list of the animals in the plural in the word list section.

Mi piacciono = I like (plural) e.g. Mi piacciono i gatti.

Non mi piacciono = I don't like (plural) e.g. Non mi piacciono i cani.

8) **Saying which animals you prefer:** Preferisco ..... (I prefer)
For saying which animal you prefer you need to say the animals in the plural:
E.g. Preferisco i cavalli.

9) **Saying if you have several pets**:
Ho = I have e.g. Ho cinque cani, Ho tre gatti....
Ask the pupils to change un to another number and to pretend they have this amount of the animals pictured.

blu

rosso

giallo

verde

bianco

nero

marrone

rosa

Making sentences with colours

When the pupils play the games, they could either practise just the vocabulary for the topic, or they could say a whole sentence. Here are some ideas of the sentences you could instruct a group, or the whole class to practise for the colours topic:

1) **Giving opinions or preference** about what colours the pupils like:
Tell the pupils in Italian the word **il** is needed after the phrases below and before the colour. **Il** is shortened to **l'** before the colour arancione.

Mi piace = I like e.g. Mi piace il verde. Mi piace il nero.

Non mi piace = I don't like e.g. Non mi piace il giallo. Non mi piace il rosso.

Preferisco = I prefer e.g. Preferisco il grigio.

Il mio colore preferito è il rosso = My favourite colour is red.

2) **Asking questions about which colours others like**: For a conversation, it is important to know how to ask questions. The games could also be played with the children forming a question as they play the games instead of just saying the colour:
Ti piace.....? = Do you like....? e.g. Ti piace il rosso?

3) **Word order for saying a colour of a noun**: Explain to the children that in Italian the colour goes after the noun. Choose an easy masculine noun like un treno (a train) and ask the children to play the games, this time saying the colour after the noun rather than just the colour e.g. un treno rosso.

Can I say 4 colours in Italian?

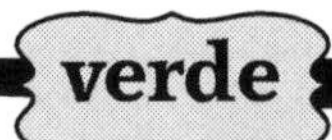

Start at “Comincia quì”, roll the dice and count that number of spaces.
Say the colour of the object you land on in Italian. Take turns to roll the dice.
To win, arrive first at “Hai vinto!”

Can I say 4 colours in Italian?

Roll the dice, and say the Italian word for the colour for the number on the dice you have thrown.
Write the Italian word for the colour or draw the picture if you haven't got this word yet. The winner is the first person to get all four colours.

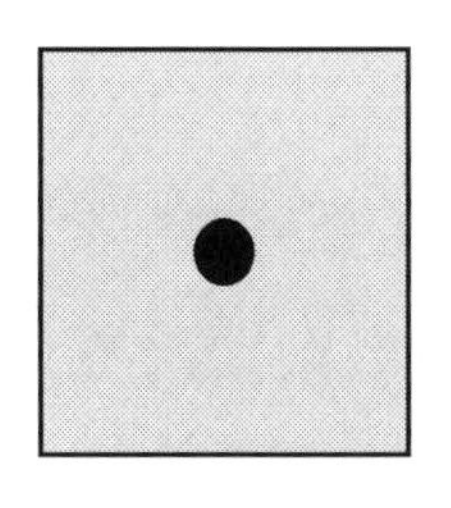

no colour this time

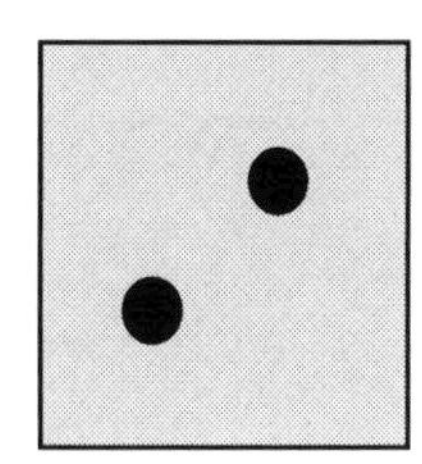

giallo

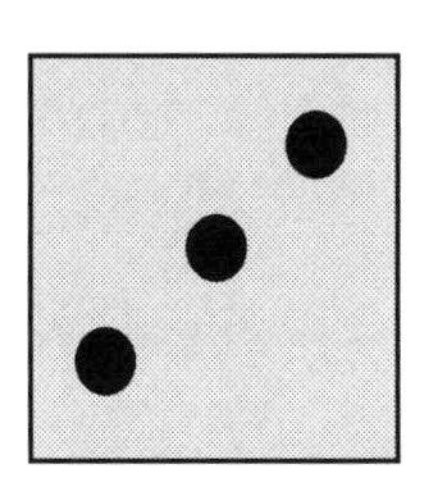

rosso

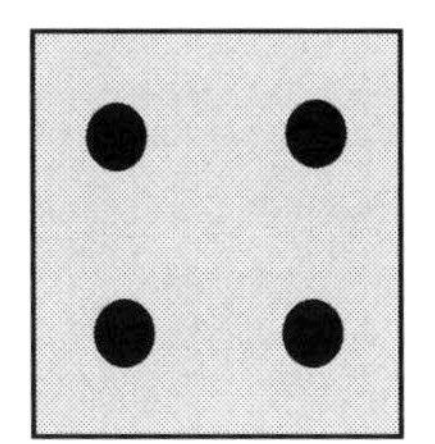

verde

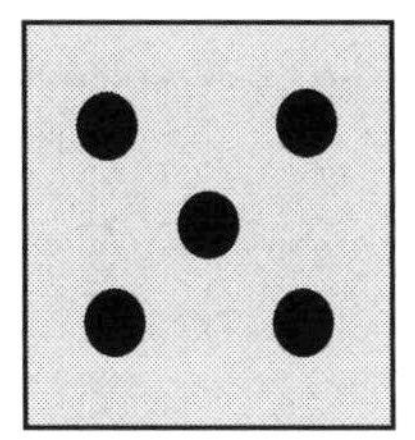

blu

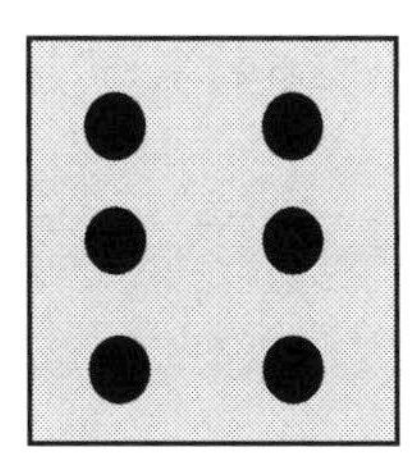

any colour
(you can choose a colour you need)

Can I say 8 colours in Italian?

Each pupil cuts out a set of dominoes by cutting along the dotted lines. Take turns to put a card down by matching a word to a picture or vice versa. If you cannot match a card, miss a turn. The winner is the person to either use all their cards, or use as many cards as possible.

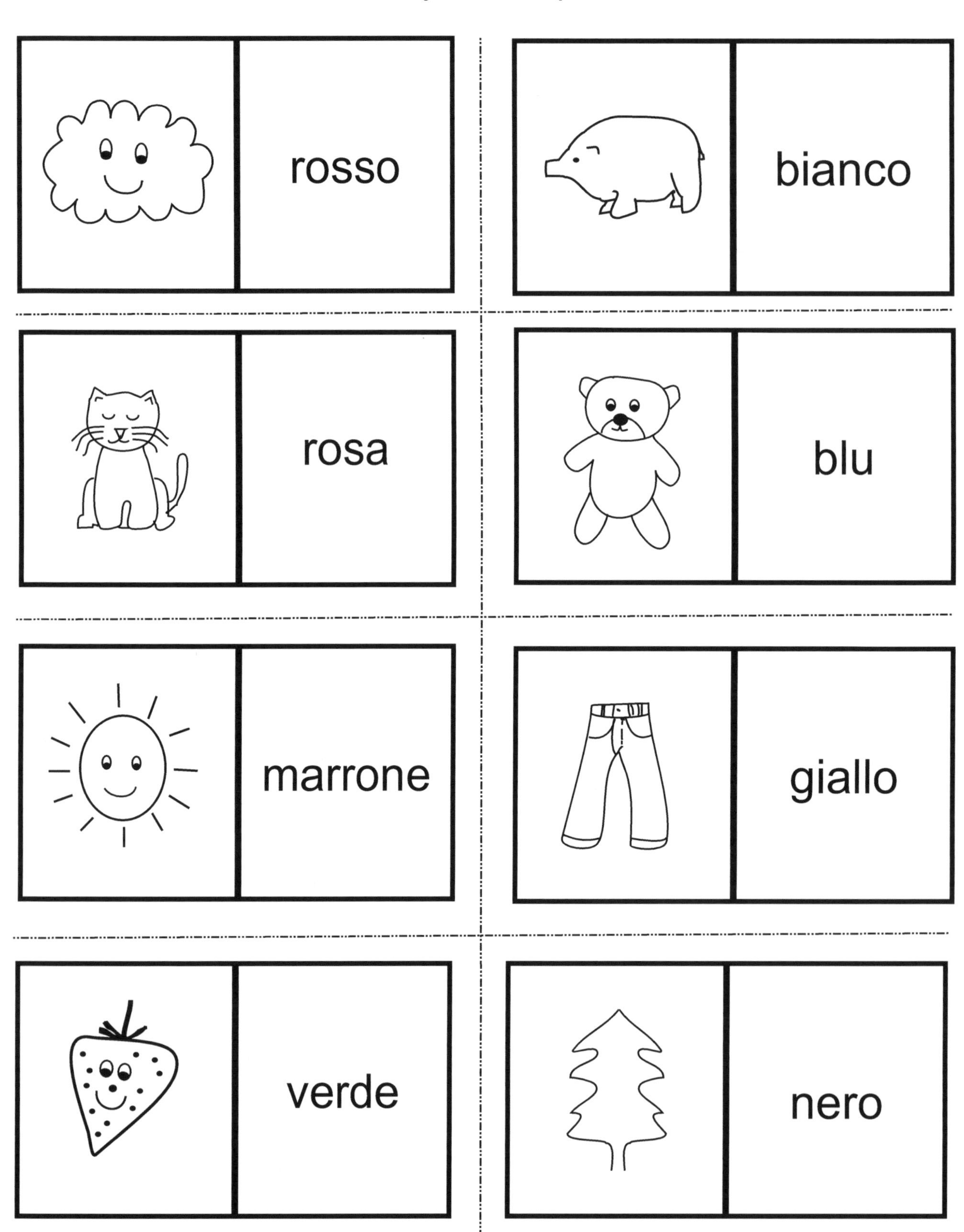

Can I say 8 colours in Italian?

Start at "Comincia quì", roll the dice and count that number of squares. If the final square has the bottom of the ladder in it go up it, or if it has the head of a snake go down it.
Say the colour of the object you land on in Italian. To win, arrive first at "Hai vinto!"

Can I say 12 colours in Italian?

rosso

Start at “Comincia quì”, roll the dice and count that number of oval shapes. Say the colour of the object you land on in Italian. To win, arrive first at “Hai vinto!”

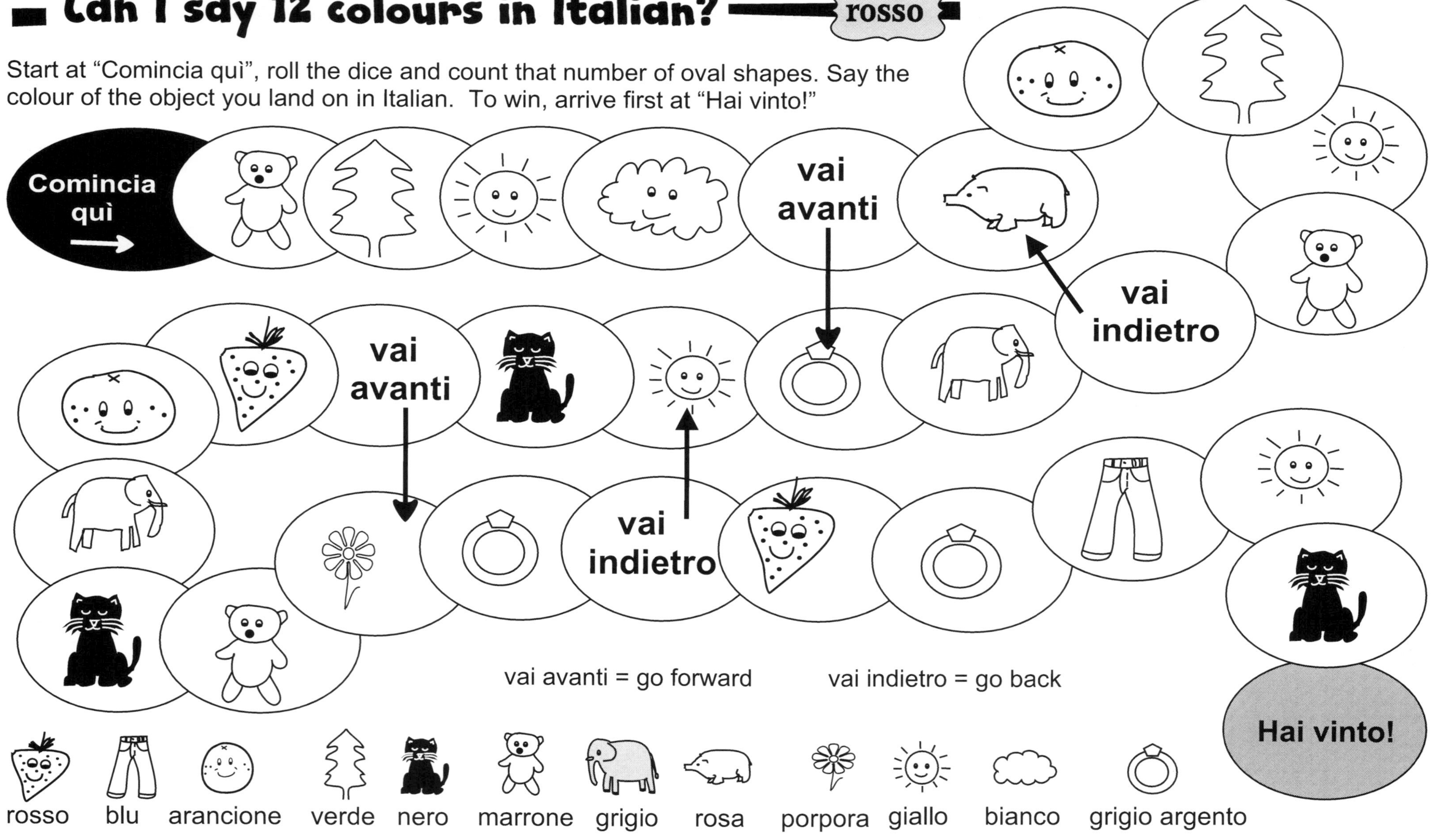

Can I say 12 colours in Italian?

rosso

Each person / team needs 5 coloured counters or cubes of one colour (or a set of noughts or a set of crosses).
Say the Italian word for the colour as you cover it with your counter.
To win you have to get 3 in a row (vertically, horizontally or diagonally).

giallo

bianco

grigio argento

rosso

blu

arancione

verde

nero

marrone

grigio

rosa

porpora

Teachers note: You could ask the pupils to match the picture mini card to the correct word card. See page 75 for pair work activities using the mini cards, and page 77 for class activities.

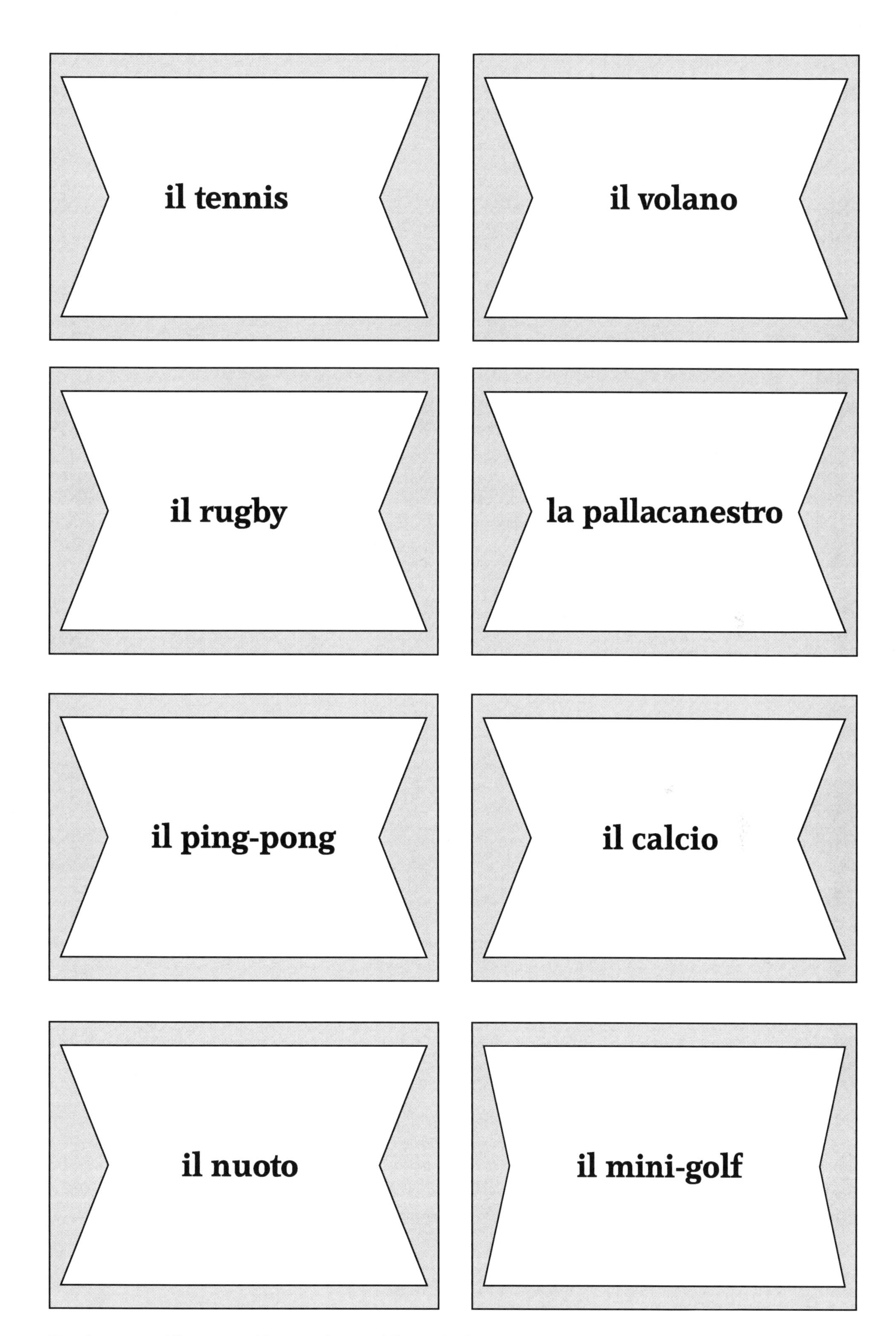

Teachers note: Photocopy this page (on card if possible), then make 8 cards by cutting round the cards. If you use card of **3 or 4 different colours** it is easier to separate the sets when handing them out to the class.

Can I say 4 sports in Italian?

Each person / team needs 5 coloured counters or cubes of one colour (or a set of noughts or a set of crosses). Say the Italian word for the sport as you cover it with your counter. To win you have to get 4 in a row (vertically, horizontally or diagonally).

il ping-pong   il tennis   il calcio   il mini-golf

Can I say 4 sports in Italian?

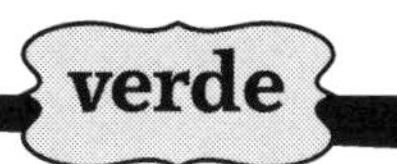

Start at "Comincia quì", roll the dice and count that number of spaces.
Say the sport you land on in Italian. Take turns to roll the dice.
To win, arrive first at "Hai vinto!"

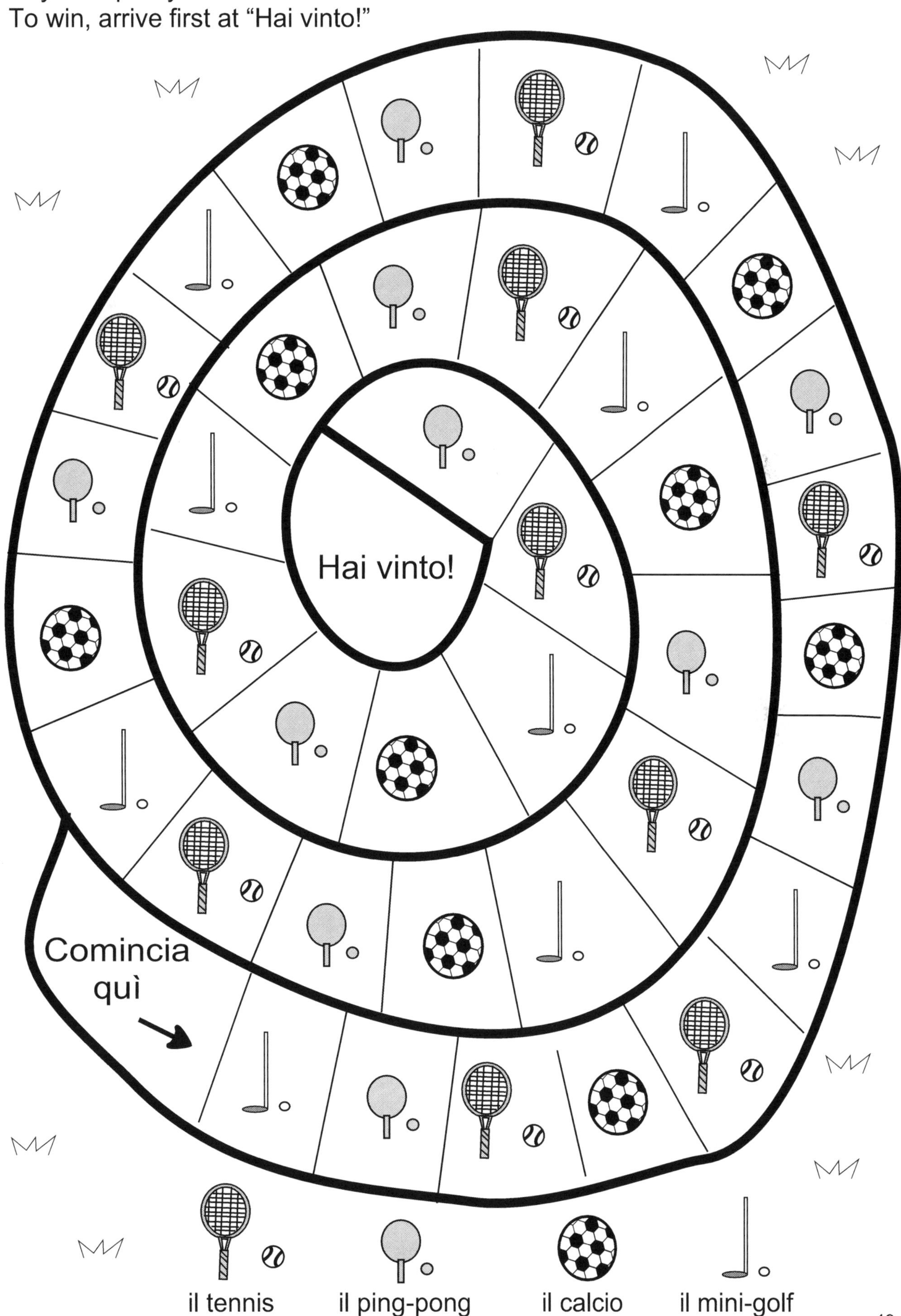

Can I say 6 sports in Italian? giallo

Start at "Comincia quì", roll the dice and count that number of spaces. Say the sport you land on in Italian. Take turns to roll the dice. To win, arrive first at "Hai vinto!"

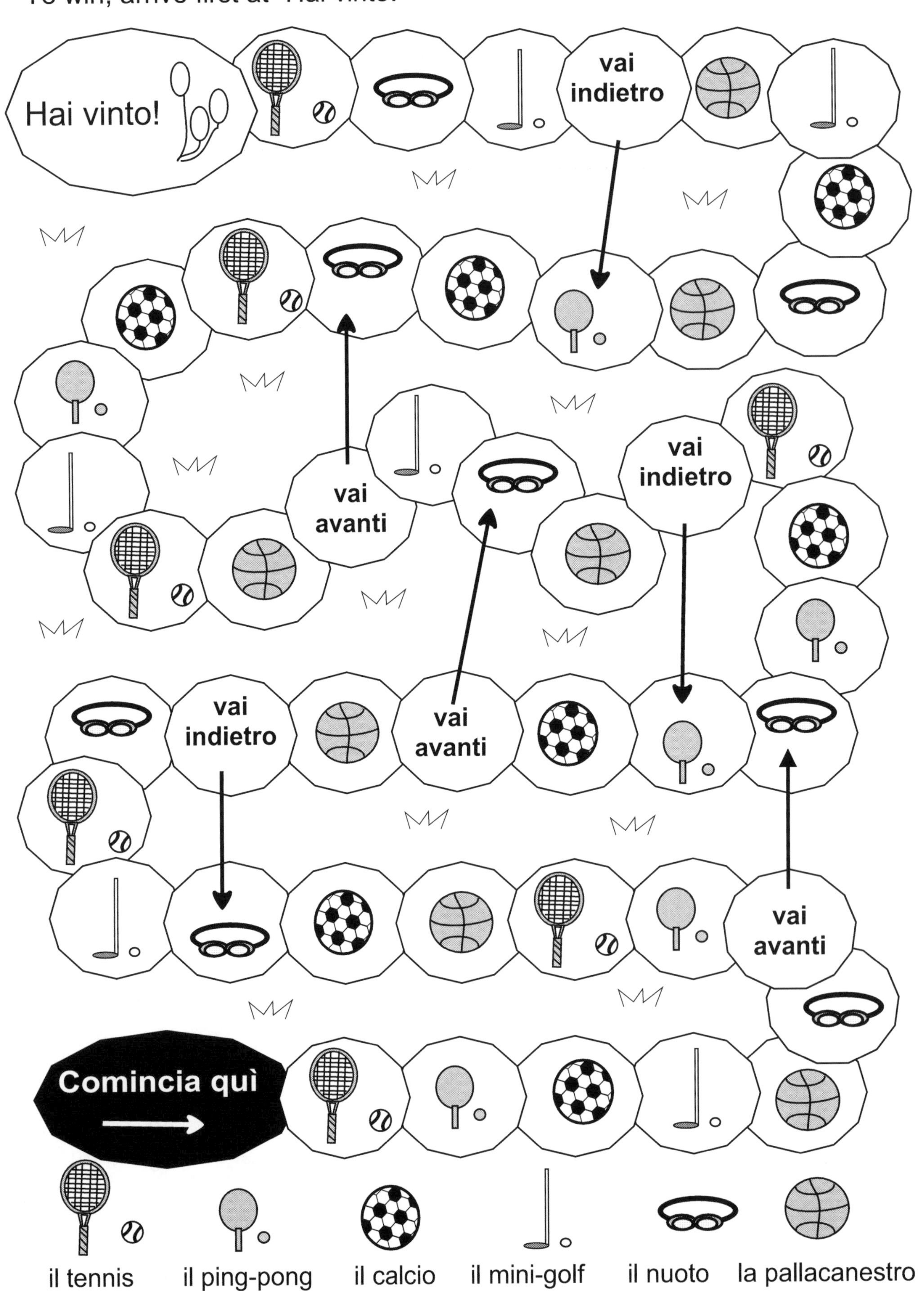

Can I say 6 sports in Italian?

Roll two dice and find the coordinate by counting along the bottom for the first dice, and up the side for the second dice. Say the sport in Italian for the coordinate to get a point, e.g 4,3 = il nuoto. If you get il calcio you get two points. To win, be the first to get 15 points.

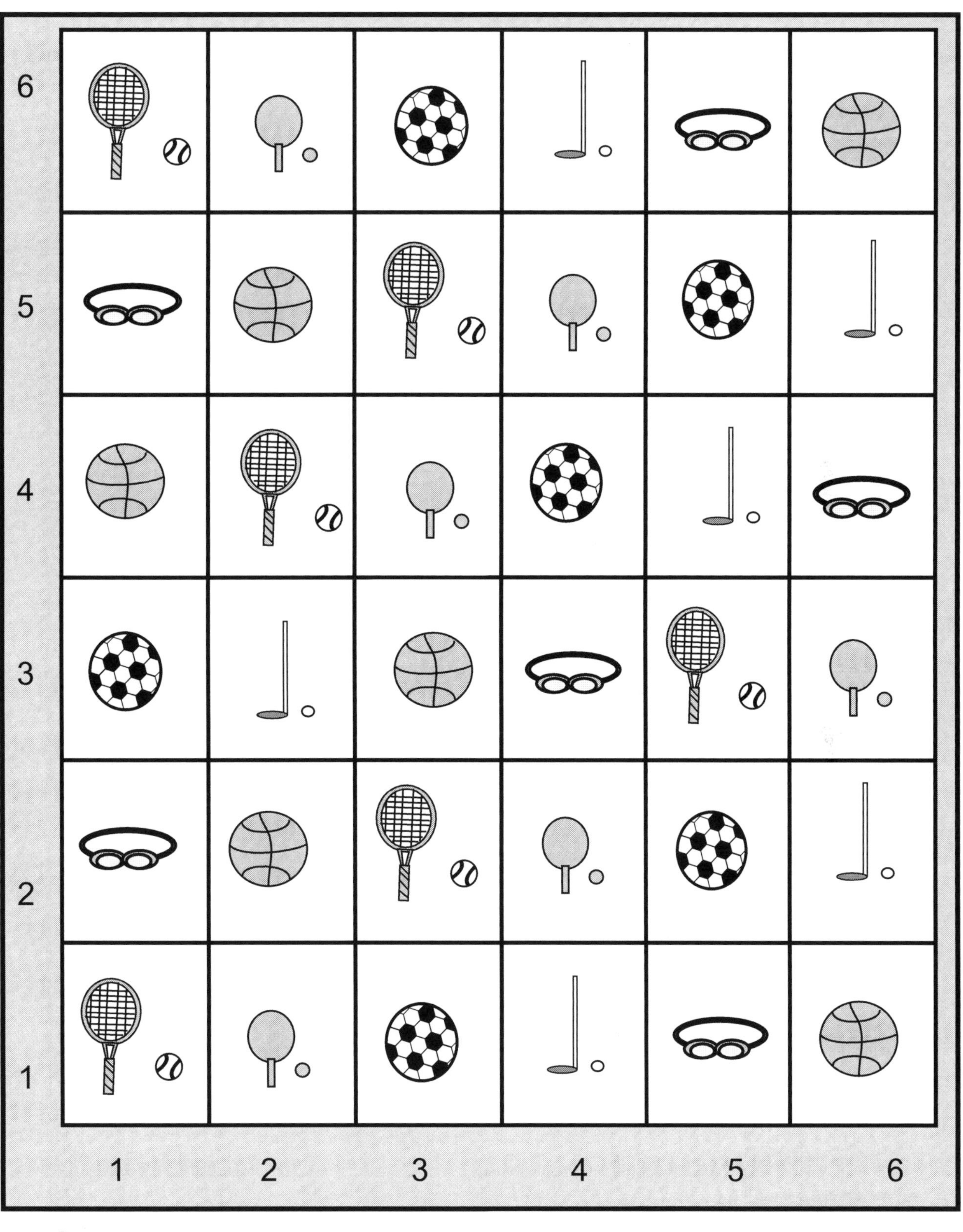

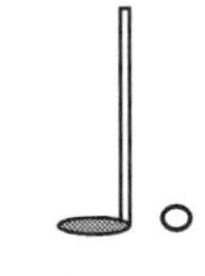

il tennis   il ping-pong   il calcio   il mini-golf   il nuoto   la pallacanestro

Can I say 8 sports in Italian?

Start at "Comincia quì", roll the dice and count that number of spaces. Say the sport you land on in Italian. Take turns to roll the dice. Each time you pass comincia quì you get a point. To win, be the first to get three points.

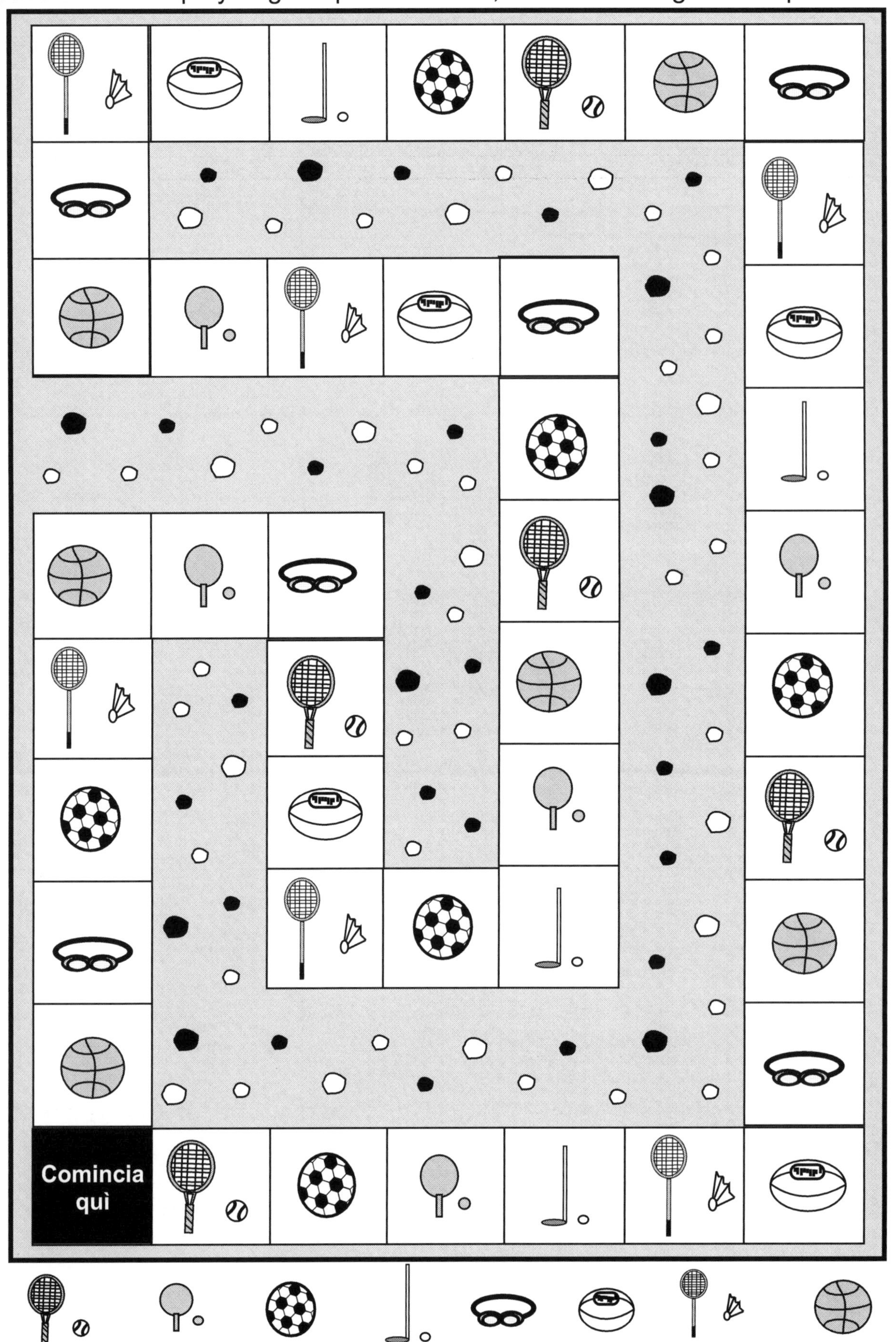

il tennis | il ping-pong | il calcio | il mini-golf | il nuoto | il rugby | il volano | la pallacanestro

Can I say 8 sports in Italian? rosso

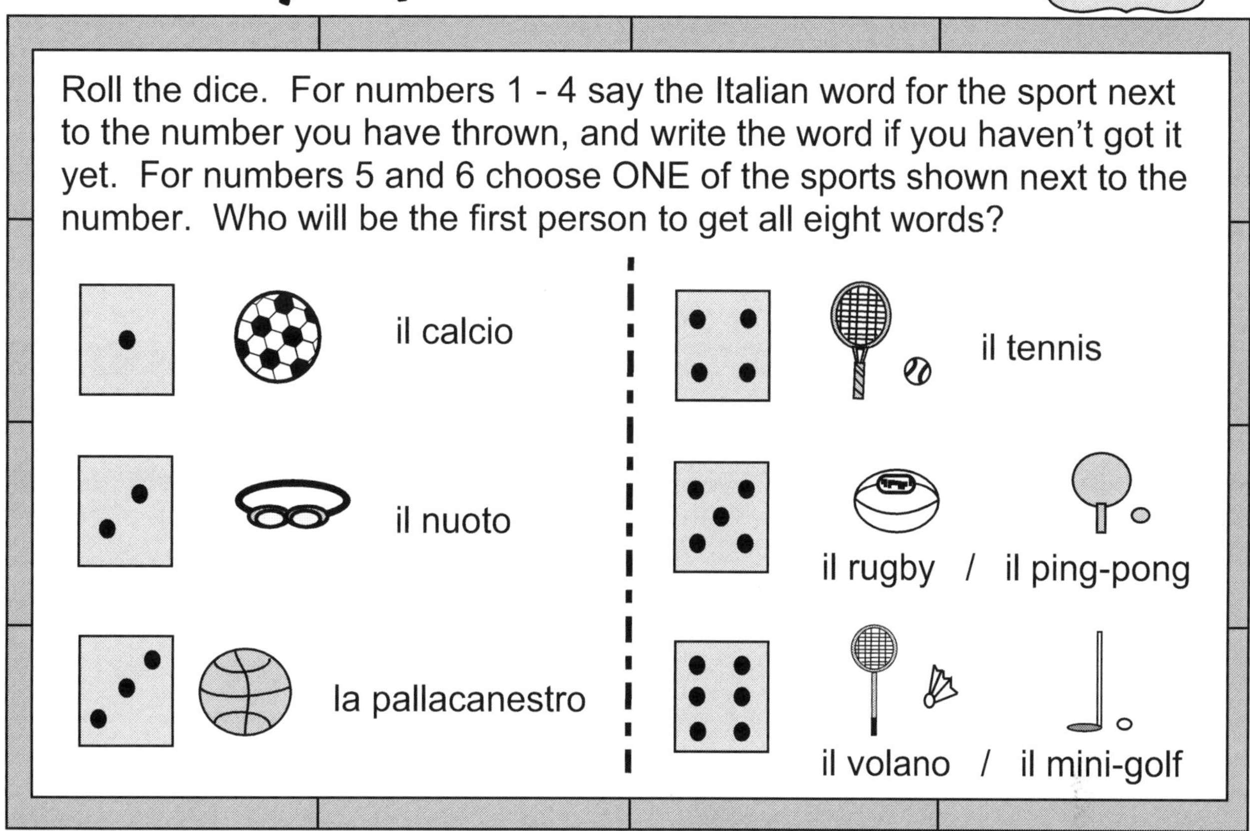

Making sentences with sports

When the pupils play the games, they could either practise just the vocabulary for the topic, or they could say a whole sentence. Here are some ideas of the sentences you could instruct a group, or the whole class to practise as they play the games:

1) **Giving opinions about which sport you like:**

Mi piace = I like e.g. Mi piace il calcio.

Non mi piace = I don't like e.g. Non mi piace il tennis.

2) **Asking others if they like certain sports:** Ti piace.....? (Do you like.....?) E.g. Ti piace il mini-golf?

3) **Saying which sports you play**: Gioco a (I play - used for the sports which use a ball or a shuttlecock.) Explain to the pupils they need to omit il or la after the phrase **gioco a** e.g. Gioco a tennis. For I swim, it's faccio nuoto.

4) **Saying when you play various sports**: Ask the pupils to make up a sentence saying when they do a particular sport.

a) **Using the days of the week**:

Lunedì .... Monday Martedì .... Tuesday Mercoledì .... Wednesday

Giovedì .... Thursday Venerdì .... Friday Sabato .... Saturday

Domenica .... Sunday E.g. Domenica gioco a mini-golf.

b) **Using seasons**: In estate = in summer In inverno = in winter
E.g. In estate gioco a tennis. In inverno gioco a calcio.

Teachers note: You could ask the pupils to match the picture mini card to the correct word card. See page 75 for pair work activities using the mini cards, and page 77 for class activities.

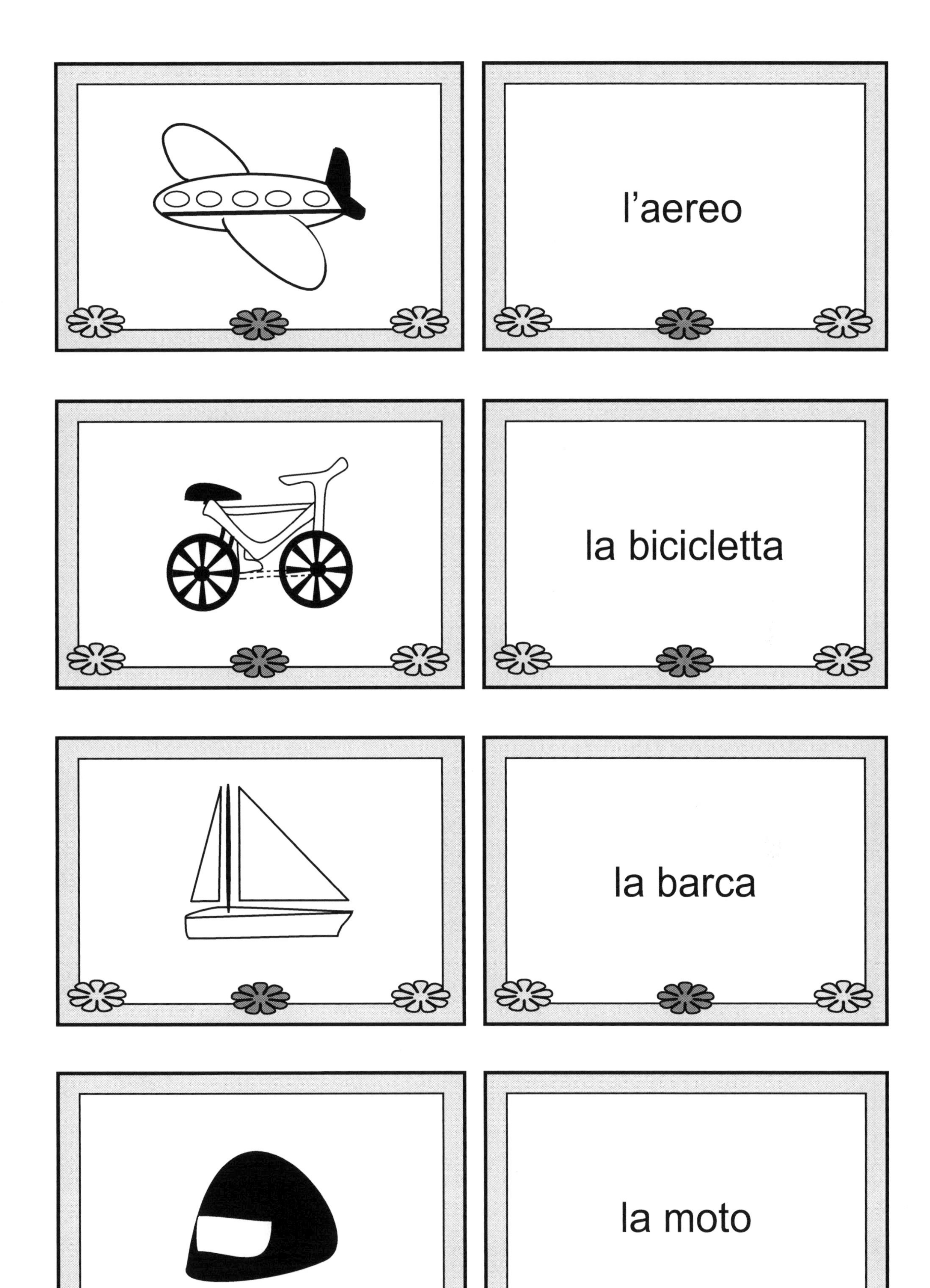

Teachers note: Photocopy this page (on card if possible), then make 8 cards by cutting round the cards. If you use card of **3 or 4 different colours** it is easier to separate the sets when handing them out to the class.

Can I say 4 types of transport in Italian? 

Start at "Comincia quì", roll the dice and count that number of squares. Say the transport you land on in Italian. To win, arrive first at "Hai vinto!"

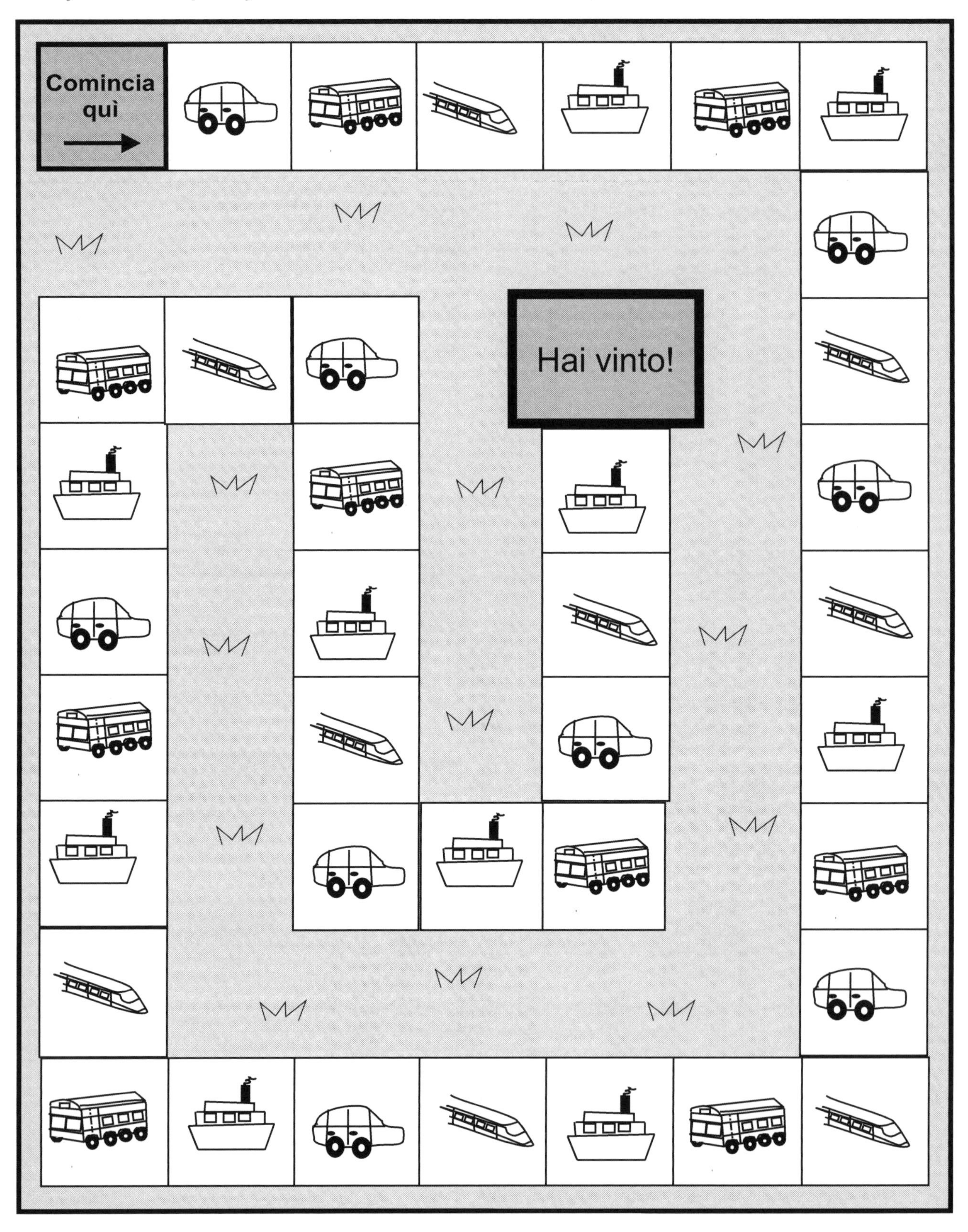

il treno

il pullman

la nave

la macchina

Can I say 4 types of transport in Italian? verde

Roll two dice and find the **coordinate** by counting along the bottom for the first dice, and up the side for the second dice. Say the transport in Italian for the coordinate to get a point, e.g. 3, 2 = la macchina The winner is the person or team who gets the most points.

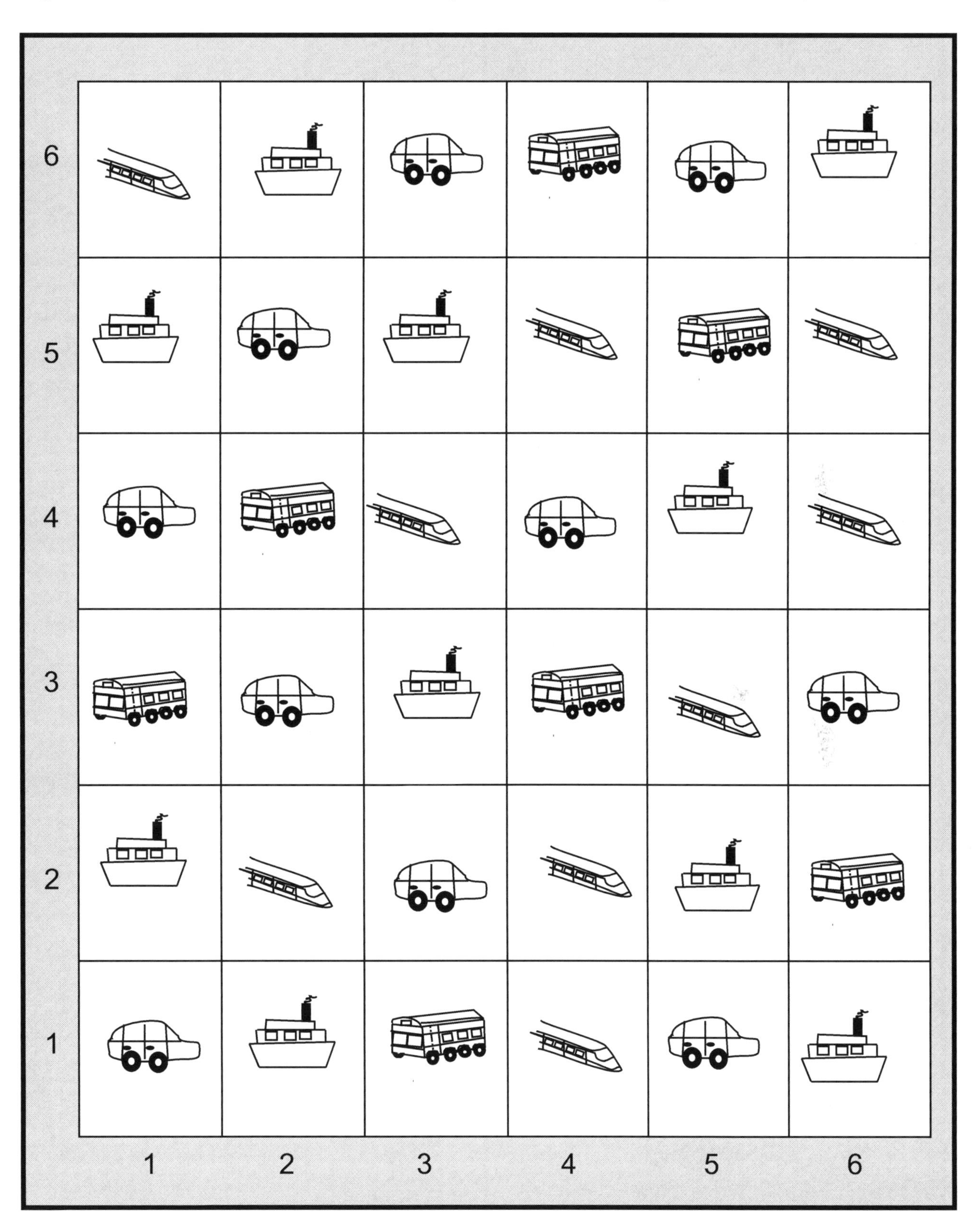

il treno

il pullman

la nave

la macchina

Can I say 6 types of transport in Italian? giallo

Start at "Comincia quì", roll the dice and count that number of squares.
Say the transport you land on in Italian. To win, arrive first at "Hai vinto!"

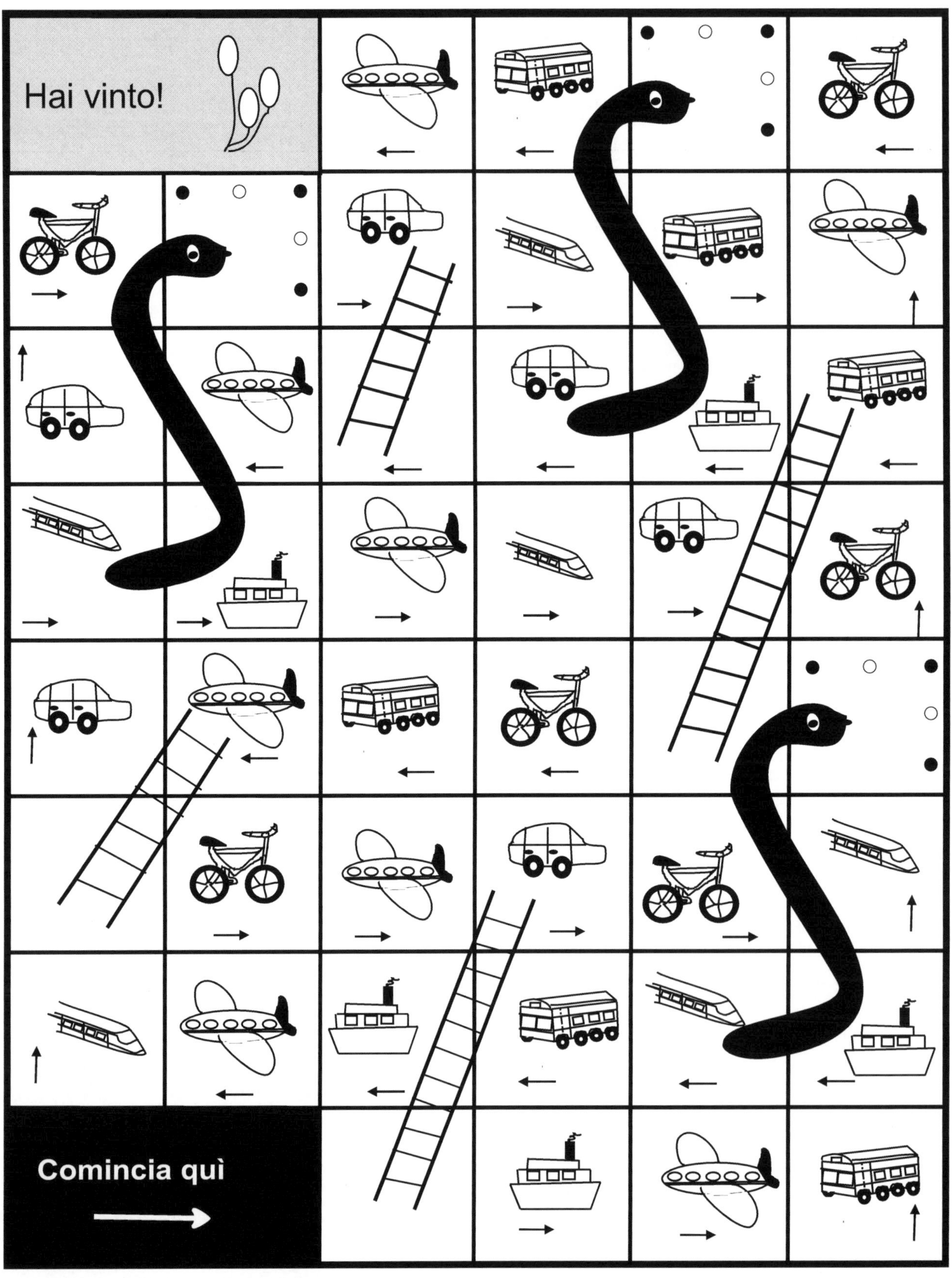

 il treno  il pullman  la nave  la macchina

l'aereo  la bicicletta

Can I say 6 types of transport in Italian?

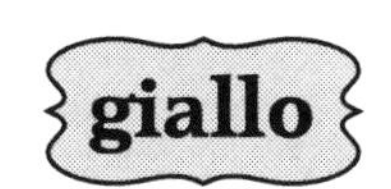

Roll the dice, and say the Italian word for the type of transport according to the number on the dice you have thrown.

Write the Italian word for the type of transport or draw it's picture if you haven't got this word yet.

The winner is the first person to get all six types of transport.

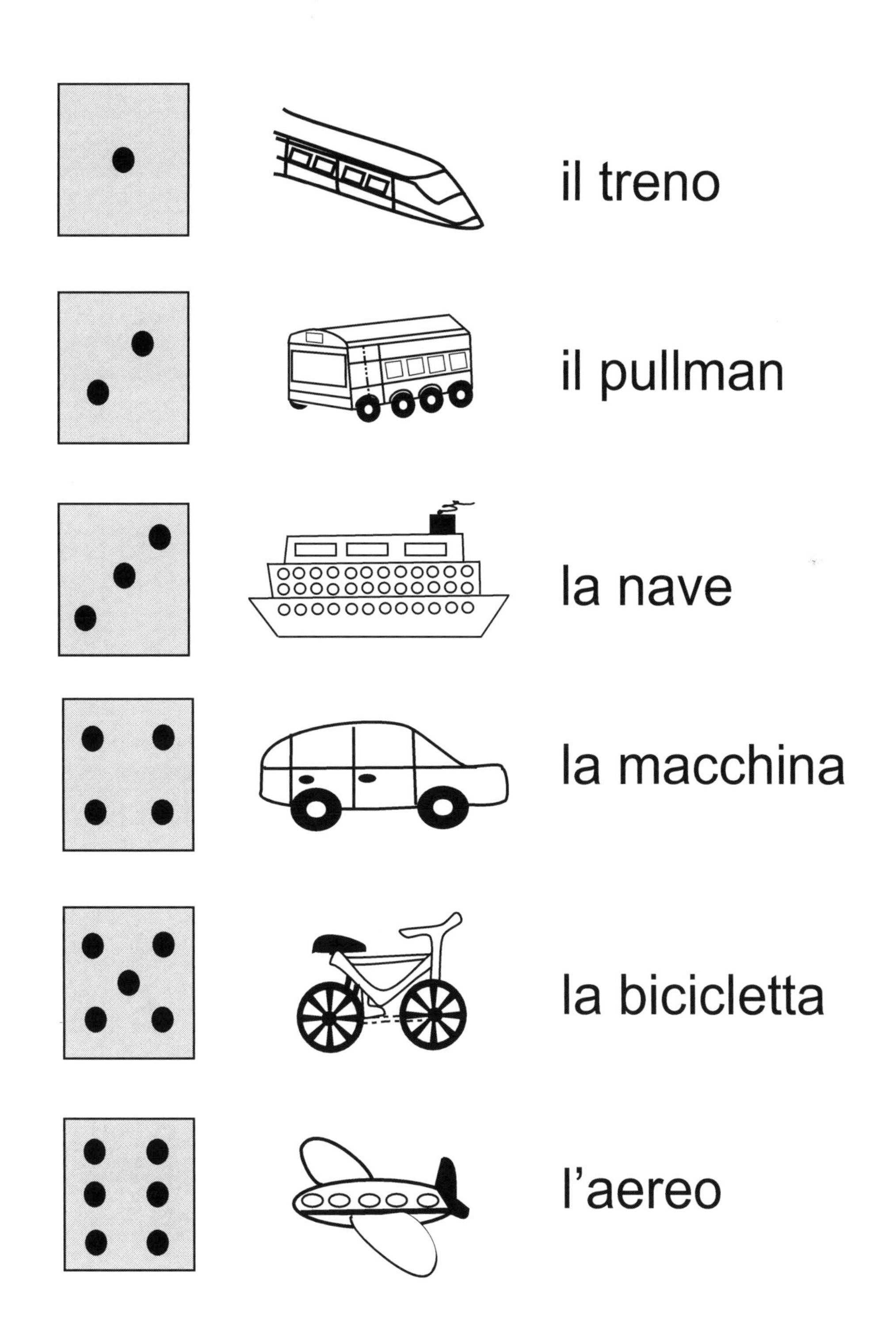

Can I say 9 types of transport in Italian?

Start at “Comincia quì”, roll the dice and count that number of spaces. Say the transport you land on in Italian.
To win, arrive first at “Hai vinto!”

Vai avanti= go forward

Vai indietro = go back

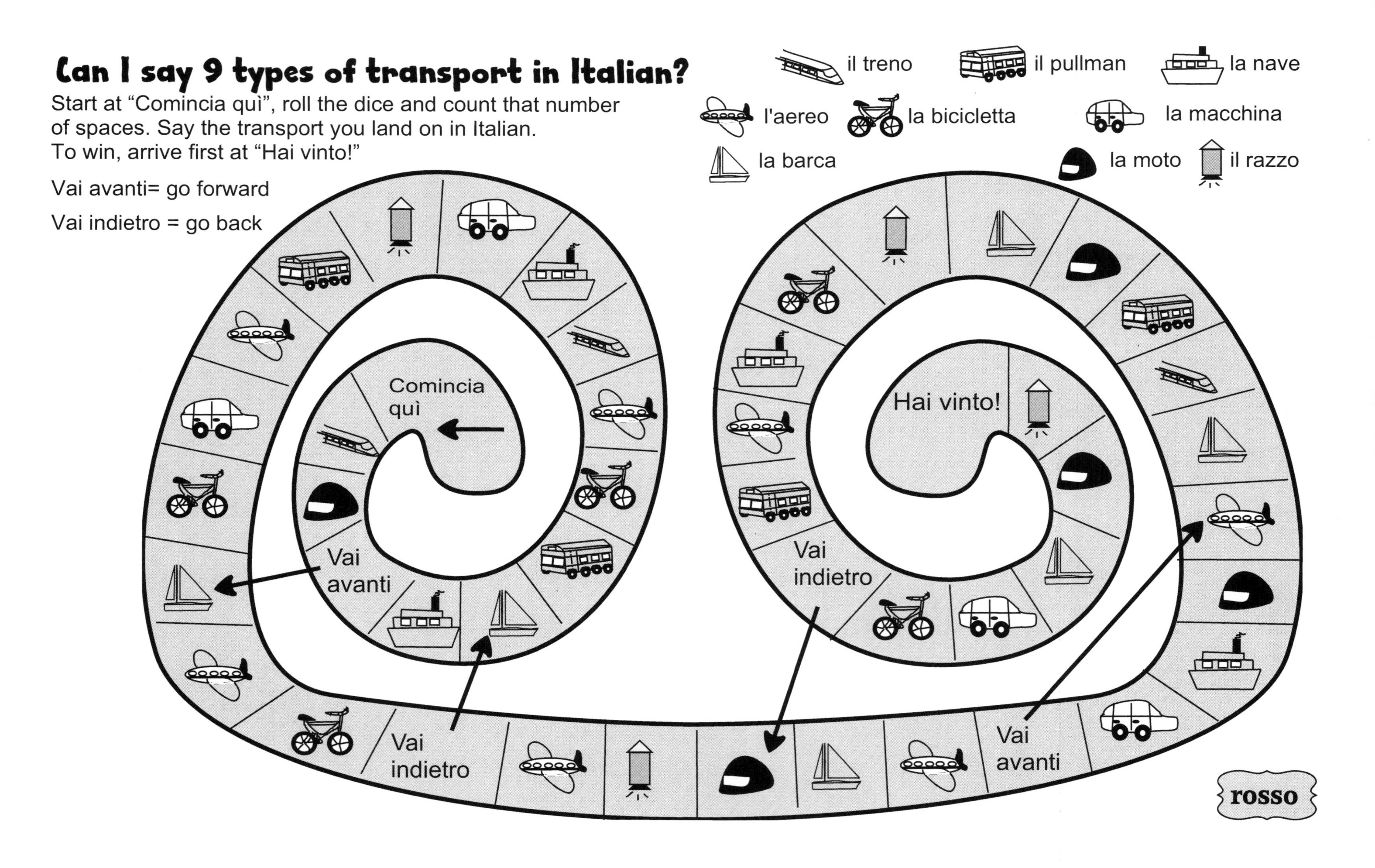

Can I say 9 types of transport in Italian? - Person A

Each pupil cuts along the dotted lines to make a set of dominoes.
Take turns to put a card down by matching a word to a picture or vice versa.
If you cannot match a card, miss a turn. The winner is the person to either use all their cards, or use as many cards as possible.

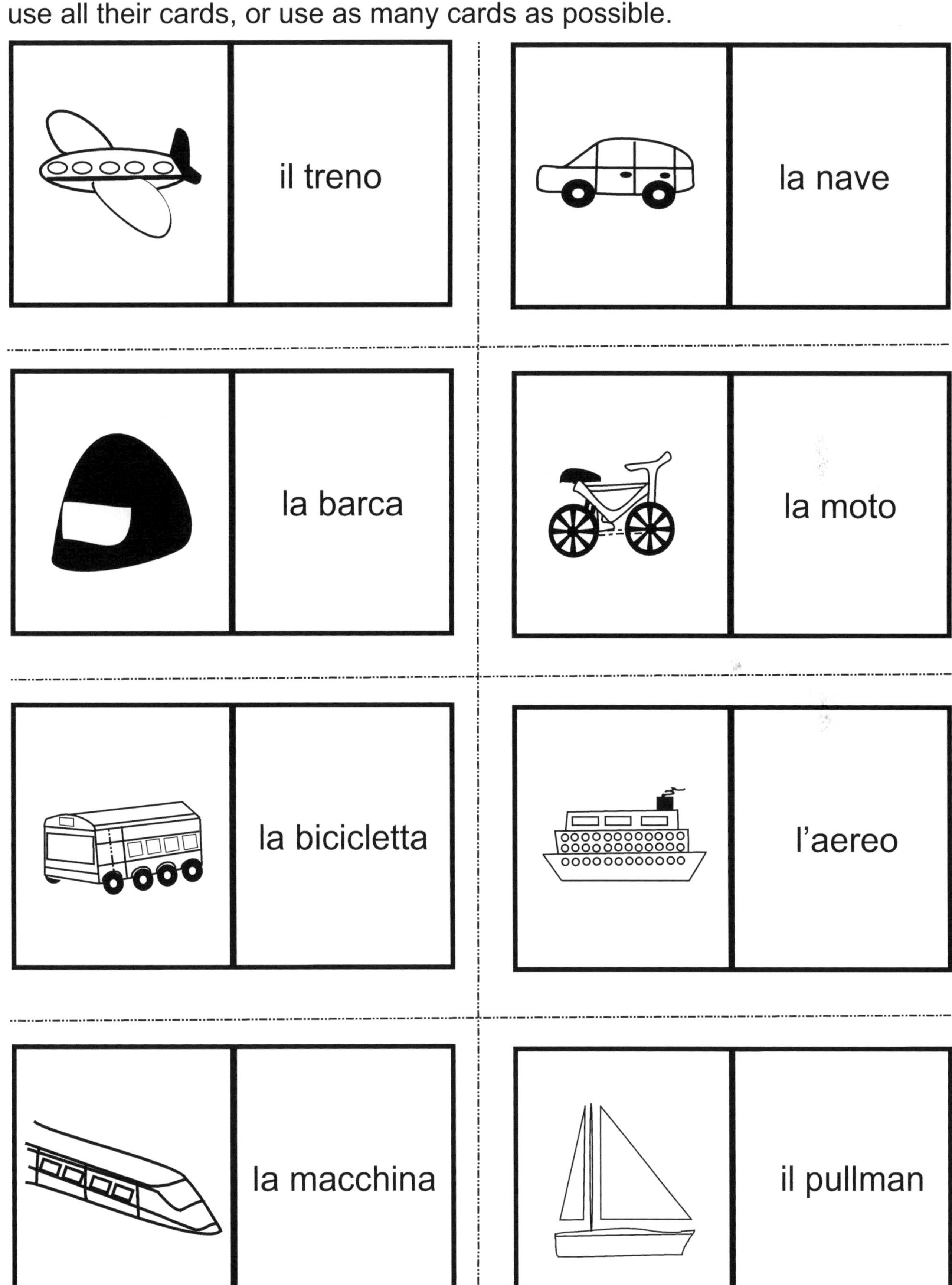

Can I say 9 types of transport in Italian? - Person B

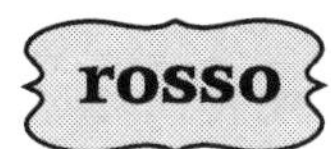

Each pupil cuts along the dotted lines to make a set of dominoes.
Take turns to put a card down by matching a word to a picture or vice versa.
If you cannot match a card, miss a turn. The winner is the person to either use all their cards, or use as many cards as possible.

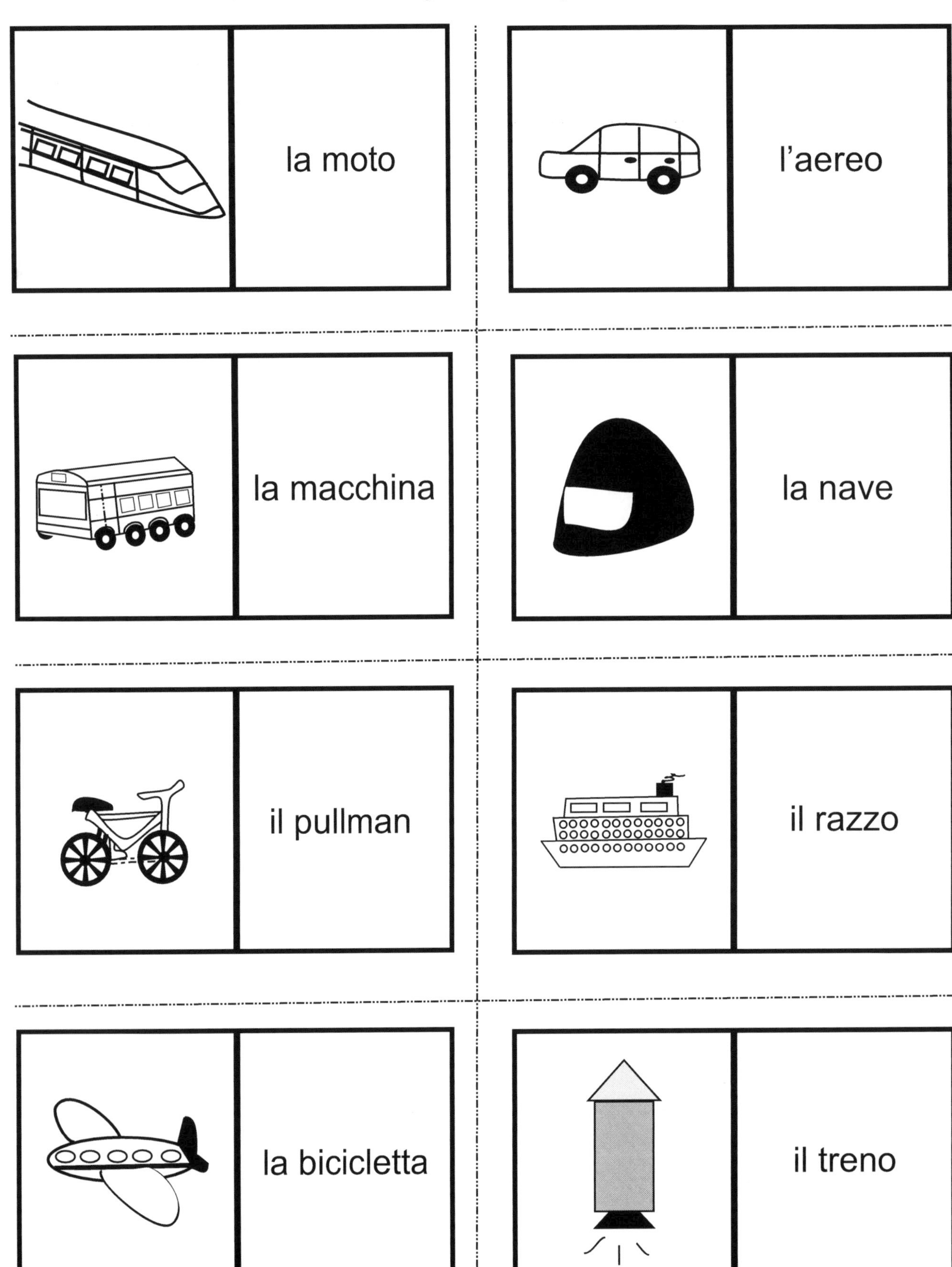

Making sentences with transport

When the pupils play the games, they could either practise just the vocabulary for the topic, or they could say a whole sentence. Here are some ideas of the sentences you could instruct a group, or the whole class to practise as they play the games:

1) **Going shopping**: Pupils ask for a toy version of the transport by saying **Vorrei …….. per favore.** (I would like…..please) e.g. Vorrei il treno, per favore. Or alternatively, just say the transport word, then add per favore (please). e.g. La macchina, per favore

2) **Describing the colour of the transport**: Pupils invent a colour for each type of transport, saying first the transport then the colour. e.g. l'aereo giallo.

Explain that for **feminine words** (la macchina , la bicicletta) the colour endings may change: e.g. la macchina nera.

Some colours change the **o** to an **a** for feminine words in the singular:
bianco > bianc**a** giallo >giall**a** rosso > ross**a** grigio > grigi**a** nero > ner**a**

Some colours stay the same for feminine words in the singular:
arancione, marrone, verde, blu, rosa, porpora

If you decide to not introduce the fact that some endings of colours change, you can instruct the pupils to say the different types of transport are one of the colours that don't change when the word is feminine. The games can be coloured in by the pupils.

3) Talking about how you like to travel: Mi piace prendere (I like to catch / travel by) e.g. Mi piace prendere il treno (I like to catch / travel by train)

4) Talking about how you travel on holiday:
Per le vacanze, prendo …….(For my holidays I travel by…..)
e.g. Per le vacanze, prendo l'aereo.

Quest'anno, per le vacanze, prendo …. … (This year, for my holidays, I travel by…)
e.g. Quest'anno per le vacanze, prendo la nave.

Teachers note: You could ask the pupils to match the picture mini card to the correct word card. See page 75 for pair work activities using the mini cards, and page 77 for class activities.

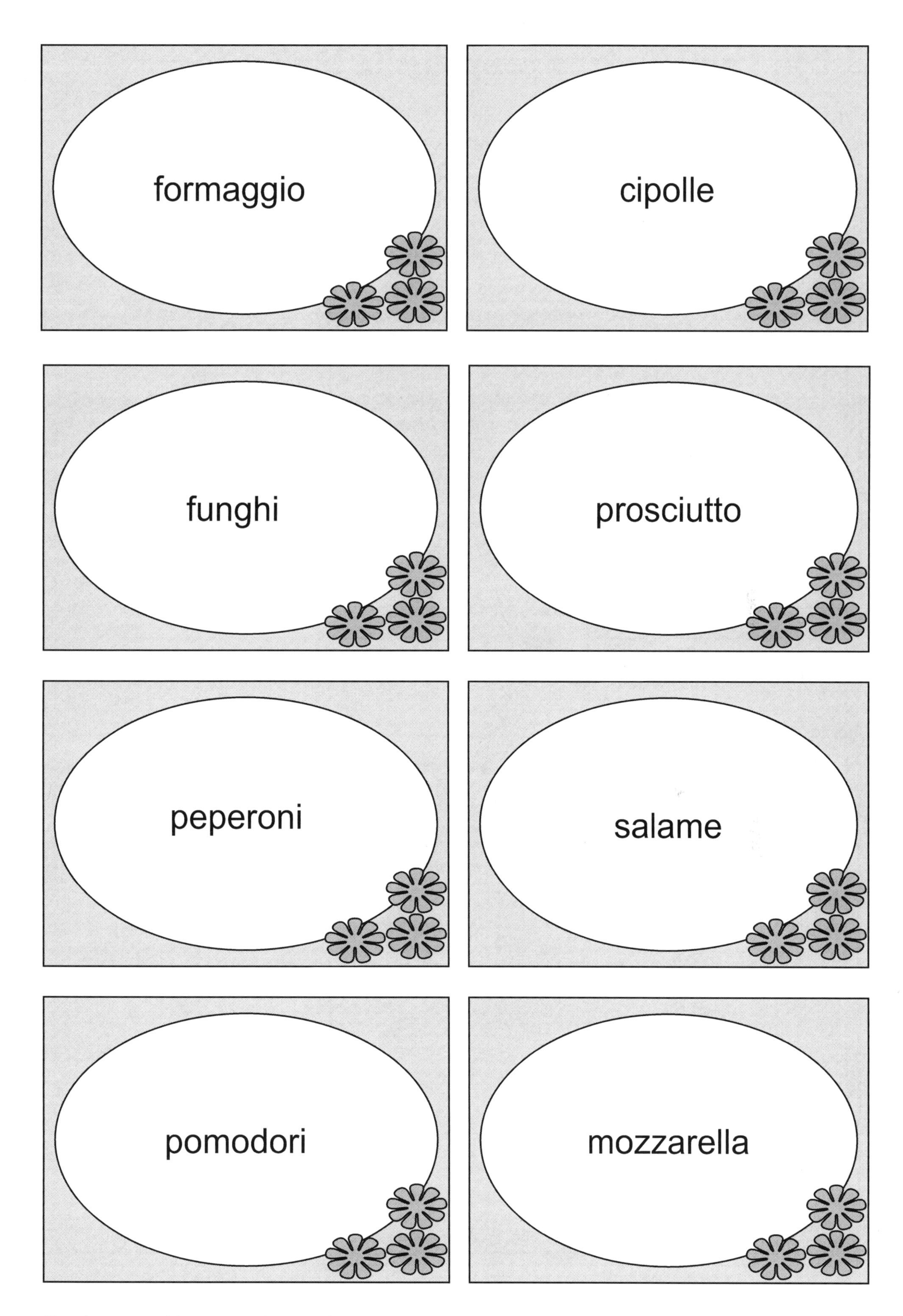

Teachers note: Photocopy this page (on card if possible), then make 8 cards by cutting round the cards. If you use card of **3 or 4 different colours** it is easier to separate the sets when handing them out to the class.

Can I say 4 pizza toppings in Italian?

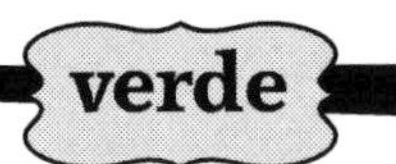

Start at "Comincia quì", roll the dice and count that number of squares.
Say the pizza topping you land on in Italian. To win, arrive first at "Hai vinto!"

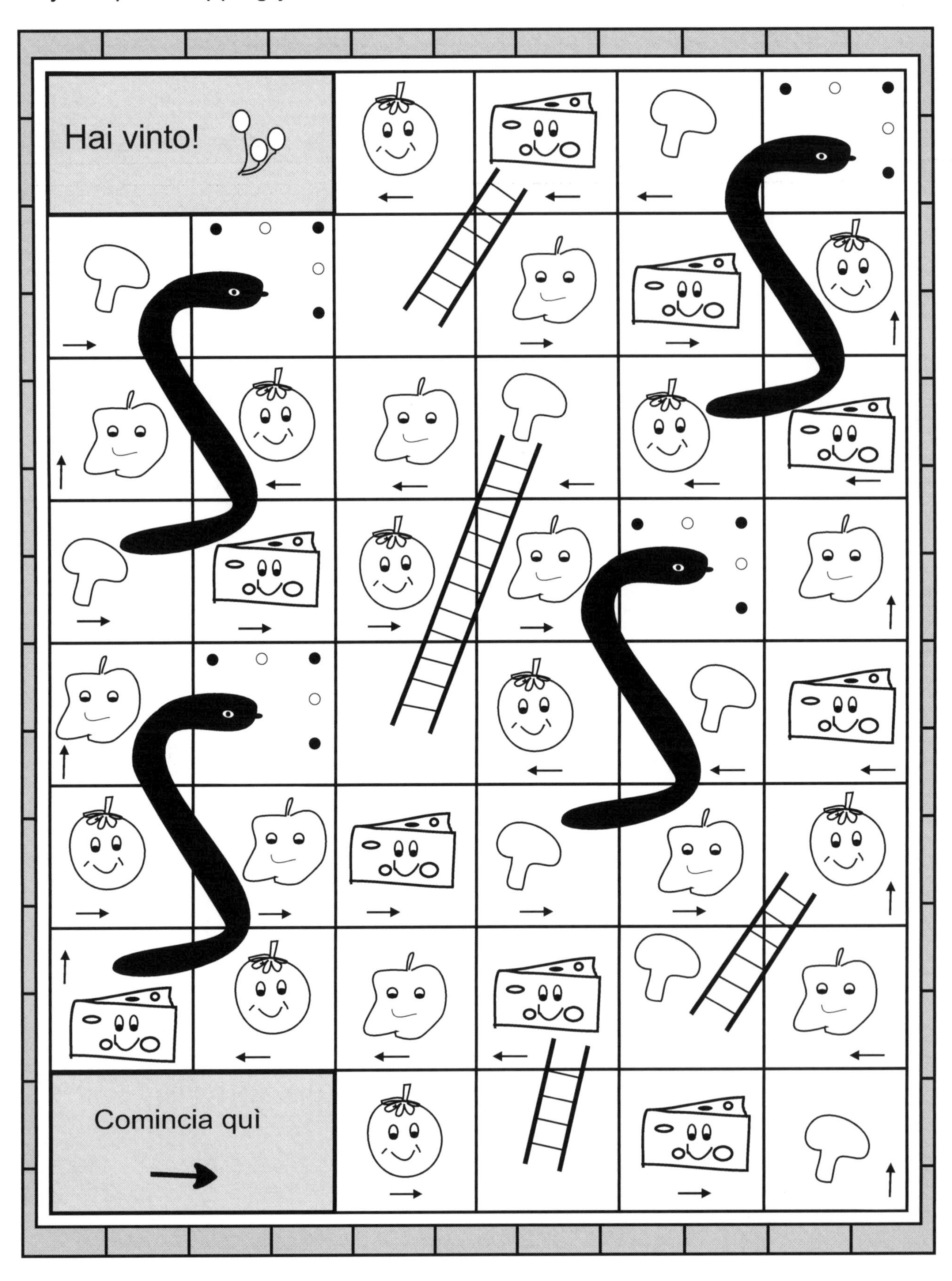

pomodori

formaggio

peperoni

funghi

Can I say 4 pizza toppings in Italian? verde

Each person / team needs 5 coloured counters or cubes of one colour (or a set of noughts or a set of crosses). Say the Italian word for the pizza topping or essential word as you cover it with your counter.
To win you have to get 3 in a row (vertically, horizontally or diagonally).

pomodori formaggio peperoni funghi

una pizza = a pizza per favore = please grazie = thank you

Buon giorno = Good day Arrivederci = Goodbye

Can I say 6 pizza toppings in Italian?

Start at "Comincia quì", roll the dice and count that number of squares. Say the number you land on in Italian. To win, arrive first at "Hai vinto!"

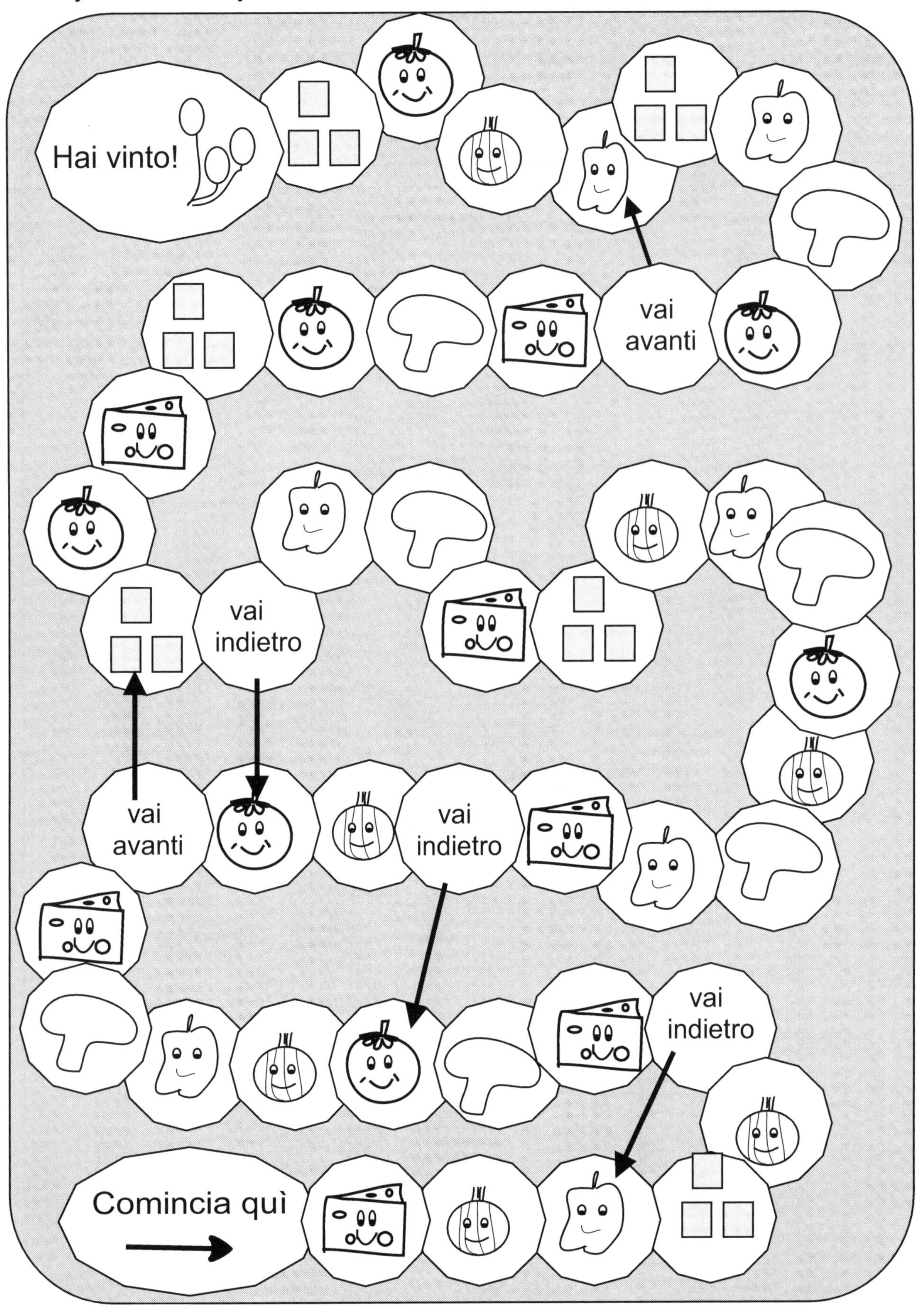

vai avanti = move forward   vai indietro = move backward

funghi pomodori formaggio cipolle peperoni prosciutto

Can I say 6 pizza toppings in Italian? giallo

Roll the dice, and draw on the pizza the pizza topping for that number if you haven't already got it. The winner is the first person to get all the pizza toppings:

⚀	pomodori	⚃	funghi
⚁	cipolle	⚄	prosciutto
⚂	peperoni	⚅	formaggio

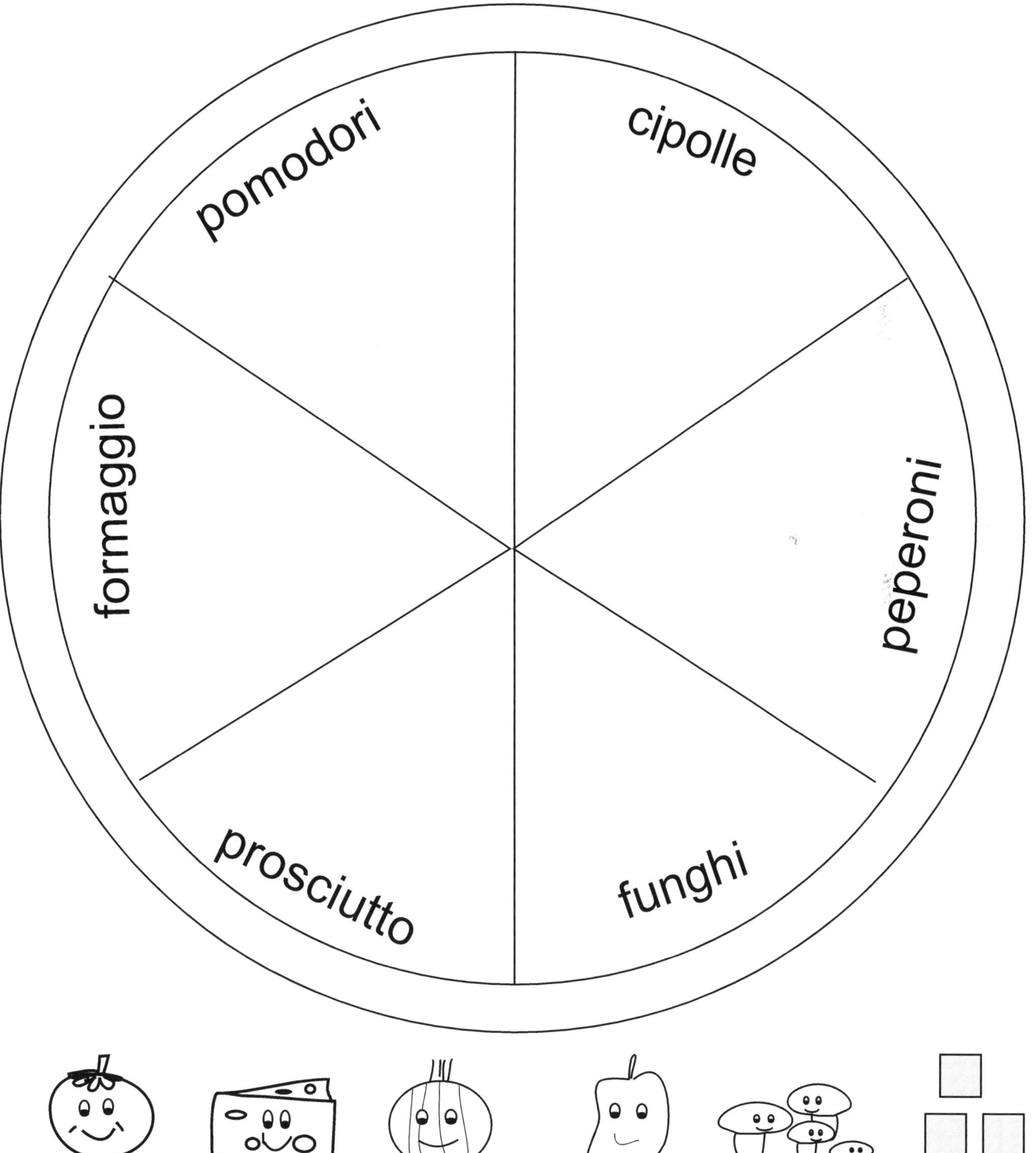

pomodori

formaggio

cipolle

peperoni

funghi

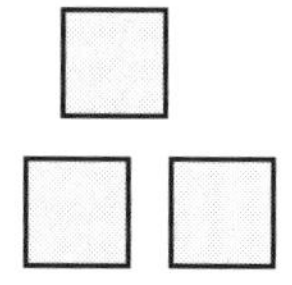
prosciutto

Can I say 9 pizza toppings in Italian?

Start at "Comincia quì", roll the dice and count that number of spaces.
Say the pizza topping you land on in Italian. To win, arrive first at "Hai vinto!"

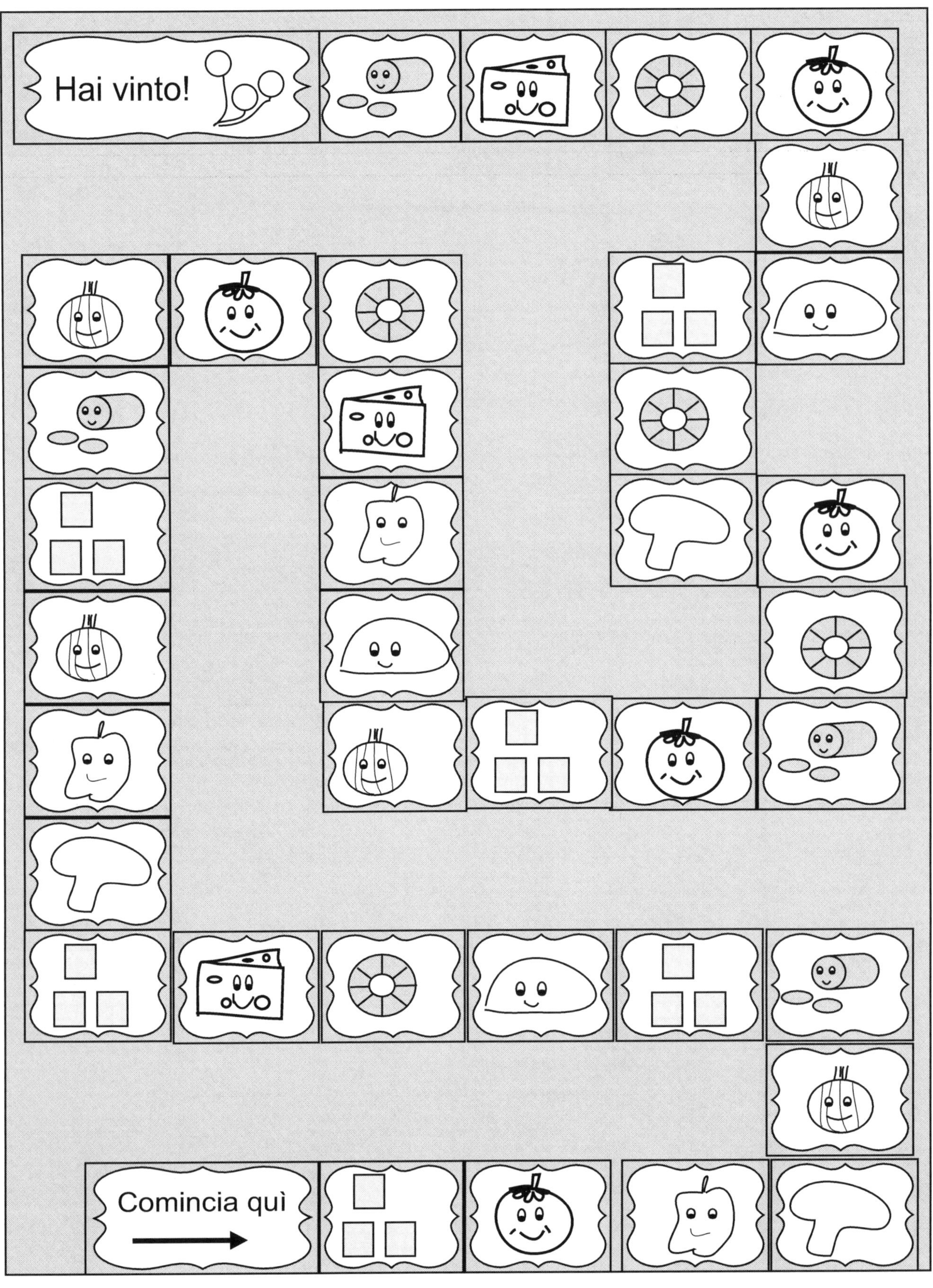

pomodori formaggio cipolle peperoni funghi
prosciutto ananas salame mozzarella

Can I say 9 pizza toppings in Italian?

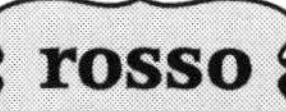

Each person / team needs 5 coloured counters or cubes of one colour (or a set of noughts or a set of crosses). Say the Italian word for the pizza topping as you cover it with your counter.
To win you have to get 3 in a row (vertically, horizontally or diagonally).

Making sentences with pizza toppings

When the pupils play the games, they could either practise just the vocabulary for the topic, or they could say a whole sentence. Here are some ideas of the sentences you could instruct a group, or the whole class to practise as they play the games:

1) **Giving opinions about which pizza toppings you like:** When the pupils play the games they could give opinions about what they like to eat.

For the pizza toppings, you need to use **Mi piace** (I like) and **Non mi piace** (I don't like) when the word is in the singular. Tell the pupils the following are in the singular:
il formaggio il prosciutto il salame la mozzarella

For the pizza toppings in the plural, tell the pupils we use **Mi piacciono** (I like) and **Non mi piacciono** (I don't like). The following pizza toppings are in the plural:
i peperoni i pomodori i funghi le cipolle

2) **Asking other if they like certain pizza toppings:**
Ti piace .....? = Do you like....? (When the word is singular)
e.g. Ti piace il salame?

Ti piacciono....? Do you like....? (When the word is plural)
e.g. Ti piacciono le cipolle?

3) **Ordering a pizza with lots of different toppings**: Ask the pupils in pairs to start with **una pizza con** and then pupil A adds a pizza topping. Pupil B repeats what pupil A says, then adds another topping. The idea of this activity is to remember the correct order of the toppings on the pizza.
e.g. Pupil A: Una pizza con pomodori
Pupil B: Una pizza con pomodori e formaggio
Pupil A: Una pizza con pomodori, formaggio e salame

Photocopiable word lists

These word lists can be photocopied for the pupils, to either learn for homework or to be stuck in the pupil's workbooks for future reference. The words are arranged so the words for "i verdi" appear first, then after a space are the extra words for "i gialli" and all the words listed are for "i rossi."

	a	the
coke	una coca-cola	la coca-cola
lemonade	una limonata	la limonata
water	un'acqua minerale	l'acqua minerale
orange juice	un succo d'arancia	il succo d'arancia
tea	un tè	il tè
coffee	un caffè	il caffè
hot chocolate	una cioccolata	la cioccoata
diet Coke	una coca-cola light	la coca-cola light
milk	un latte	il latte

la mela............the apple
la banana........the banana
il kiwi..............the kiwi
il melone ....the melon

la fragola.........the strawberry
l'arancia..........the orange

la pera............the pear
il limone..........the lemon

le mele.........the apples
le banane......the bananas
i kiwi ....the kiwis
i meloni........the melons

le fragole ......the strawberries
le arance ......the oranges

le pere..........the pears
i limoni.........the lemons

1	2	3	4	5	6	7	8	9	10	11	12
uno	due	tre	quattro	cinque	sei	sette	otto	nove	dieci	undici	dodici

un gatto.......... a cat
un cane.......... a dog
un pesce......... a fish
un serpente..... a snake

un coniglio....... a rabbit
un cavallo....... a horse

un uccello .... a bird
una tartaruga... a tortoise
un topo.......... a mouse

i gatti............. the cats
i cani............. the dogs
i pesci............ the fishes
i serpenti......... the snakes

i conigli........... the rabbits
i cavalli........... the horses

gli uccelli......... the birds
le tartarughe..... the tortoises
i topi............... the mice

rosso .... red
blu .... blue
giallo................ yellow
verde............... green

nero................. black
bianco .... white
marrone .... brown
rosa .... pink

porpora .... purple
grigio .... grey
arancione .... orange
grigio argento.... silver

il calcio .... football
il tennis .... tennis
il mini-golf.......... mini-golf
il ping-pong........ table tennis

il nuoto.............. swimming
il volano.. .... badminton

il rugby .... rugby
la pallacanestro.. basketball

il treno.......... the train
il pullman....... the bus
la nave.......... the ship
la macchina.... the car

l'aereo.......... the plane
la bicicletta..... the bike

la moto.......... the motorbike
la barca .... the small boat
il razzo .... the rocket

il formaggio......cheese
i funghi............mushrooms
i pomodori....... tomatoes
i peperoni........ peppers

il prosciutto...... ham
le cipolle..........onions

il salame..........salami
la mozzarella....mozzarella
l’ananas..........pineapple

Pair work activities using the mini cards

The idea of these games is to speak Italian, so remember to speak Italian as you enjoy the games. You may choose one of these games:

Accoppia! (Pairs card game)

Place all the cards face down on the table. With a partner, take turns to turn over two cards.

If you find a matching pair you "win" the cards.

The idea of the game is to try and find as many pairs as possible. Say the Italian words for the cards as you turn over the cards.

Indovina la carta (Guess the card)

In pairs, each person takes a card. Make sure your partner does not see your card! Take turns to guess each other's card.

If you guess the card correctly, you "win" the card. Each person then takes a new card. Take turns to guess each other's card. The winner is the person who wins the most cards.

Sono andato al mercato e ho comprato ....

(I went to the market and bought _)

In pairs, take it in turns to say **C'è** (there is), then add a card of your own choice and place this card face down on the table.

The next person has to repeat **C'è** and the previous card or cards that were said before saying **e** (and) and then their choice of word, and placing this word also face down next to the previous card or cards.

Try not to look at the cards that are face down on the table unless you need to check the word after it has been said. For example:
Person A : **C'è** la macchina
Person B : **C'è** la macchina e il treno
Person A : **C'è** la macchina, il treno e la nave

Come si dicono le parole?

(How do you say the words?)

Put all the cards together in a pile, and shuffle the cards. Take it in turns with a partner to take a card: If it is a picture card, say the Italian word for the card. If it is a Italian word, say what it means in English.

If you know the word you "win" the card. If you don't know the word put the card in a separate pile and at the end of the game check what it means. The idea of the game is to win as many cards as possible.

Qual è la parola italiana?

(What Italian word is it?)

In pairs, pupil A takes a card and draws a picture for this word on a whiteboard. Pupil B has to guess in Italian the word. Then swap roles.

È maschile o femminile?
(Is it masculine or feminine?)

Using the mini cards, arrange the cards according to if the words are masculine (boy words) or feminine (girl words).

Masculine words start with either **un** / **uno** (a) or **il / lo** (the) or **i / gli** (the plural)

Feminine words start with either **una** (a) or **la** (the) or **le** (the plural)

Le opinioni (opinions)

Take turns to turn over a mini card and say if you like or dislike the thing pictured:
Mi piace / Mi piacciono...... I like

Non mi piace / Non mi piacciono .... I don't like

For colours you need the word **il** before the colour, but for arancione it needs to be **l'** as it starts with a.
Mi piace / Non mi piace is used when the word that follows is in the singular.
Mi piacciono/ Non mi piacciono is used when the word that follows is in the plural.
E.g. Mi piace la coca-coca.
Mi piacciono i pomodori.

Scatto (snap)

Divide the cards equally between 2 people. Take turns to say the Italian word for the card as you place the card face up on the table. You will need to make a pile of cards each so that you can see if two cards are the same.

If the two top cards are the same, to win both piles of cards you have to be the first person to say the Italian word for the top card as you place your hand down on the pile of cards.

il campionato (the championship)

Working as a class or in table groups, two pupils compete at the same time to translate the word first from Italian to English, or vice versa. The two pupils who are competing stand up by their chair, and they do not need to put up their hand to answer as they can just call out the answer. One person has the mini cards and says whatever is on the top card. Whoever says the word first out of the two competitors stays on, and a new person then stands up to take on the winner. Time the game, and after 5 minutes, whoever wins the final round is the champion.

Mimos (Mimes)

Sport, transport or Animals topic
In pairs, take it in turns to take a card to mime the sport or animal for your partner to guess in Italian.

Quale manca? (Which one is missing?)

Put all the picture cards face up on the table. Pupil A closes their eyes and pupil B takes away one card. Pupil A has to say which card is missing in Italian. Then swap roles.

Teacher's note: Choose how many words you want each group of children to practise, and give the pupils the mini cards for their group, or ask the children to find their words from the whole set they are given. See page 1 for ideas of how to differentiate the topics to three levels. Then, either instruct them an activity to do, or photocopy the above instructions. The pupils will need two sets of cards for the dominoes or pairs card game.

Class activities using the mini cards

Trova la carta uguale (Find the matching card)

Give the pupils a card each and then ask them to circulate in the room saying the Italian word for their card. The pupils need to find either the person who has the picture card for their word card, and vice versa, or the person with the same card.

This game can use either just one topic (but have several cards for each word so there are enough cards for the whole class or group) or can be used as revision for various topics. Once the pupils have found a match they could either get a new card from the teacher, or be asked to sit down and draw and label their word on a whiteboard.

Prendiamo una pizza o qualcosa da bere! (Lets have a pizza or a drink!)

Half of the class are waiters / waitresses and have the mini cards for either the drinks or pizzas or both. The other half of the class are customers. Waiters and waitresses go to the customers who are seated around the room. Customers can only order one thing from each waiter or waitress, but can be served by various waiters / waitresses. Customers receive the mini card for what they order. Customers can ask for the card by adding **per favore** (please) after the Italian word for what they order or by saying **Vorrei __ per favore** (I would like _ please).

Note to teachers: If the mini cards are being handed out to the customers, you may need several sets of cards per waiter / waitress or you can give some blank cards for any extra cards the pupils need.

Mostrami..... (show me)

In table groups / as a whole class everyone has a set of mini cards.

The teacher says **Mostrami** then one of the Italian words.
The pupils compete to be the first to hold up the correct card.

If you are playing this game with the whole class you can differentiate this activity by giving the pupils the cards for the suggested key words for their group (verde, giallo, rosso) as shown at the front of this book on page 1. Then, before you say Mostrami, you could tell the class if this time it's for i verdi/ i gialli / i rossi.

Attività scritta (Written activity)

Ask the pupils to randomly choose a mini card and then write a sentence in Italian on a whiteboard / in their book. Tell the pupils if any of the mini cards appear twice, they do not need to do the sentence again.)

La matematica (maths)

The teacher says a simple maths equation, and the class has to hold up the card which is that answer.

E.g. due più due (2 + 2)
answer: quattro

Also available by Joanne Leyland:

French
Young Cool Kids Learn French
Cool Kids Speak French (books 1, 2 & 3)
French Word Games - Cool Kids Speak French
40 French Word Searches Cool Kids Speak French
First 100 Words In French Coloring Book Cool Kids Speak French
Cool Kids Speak French - Special Christmas Edition
Photocopiable Games For Teaching French
On Holiday In France Cool Kids Speak French
Cool Kids Do Maths In French
Un Alien Sur La Terre
Le Singe Qui Change De Couleur
Tu As Un Animal?

The word search editions have 40 topics in each book. The word searches are in fun shapes. Pictures accompany the words to find.

The first 100 words colouring book editions have 3 or 4 words per page, and are ideal for those who like to colour as they learn.

Italian
Young Cool Kids Learn Italian
Cool Kids Speak Italian (books 1, 2 & 3)
Italian Word Games - Cool Kids Speak Italian
40 Italian Word Searches Cool Kids Speak Italian
First 100 Words In Italian Coloring Book Cool Kids Speak Italian
On Holiday In Italy Cool Kids Speak Italian
Photocopiable Games For Teaching Italian
Un Alieno Sulla Terra
La Scimmia Che Cambia Colore
Hai Un Animale Domestico?

The stories in a foreign language have an English translation at the back.

German
Young Cool Kids Learn German
Cool Kids Speak German (books 1, 2 & 3)
German Word Games - Cool Kids Speak German
40 German Word Searches Cool Kids Speak German
First 100 Words In German Coloring Book Cool Kids Speak German

If you like games, you could try the word game editions.

Spanish
Young Cool Kids Learn Spanish
Cool Kids Speak Spanish (books 1, 2 & 3)
Spanish Word Games - Cool Kids Speak Spanish
40 Spanish Word Searches Cool Kids Speak Spanish
First 100 Words In Spanish Coloring Book Cool Kids Speak Spanish
Cool Kids Speak Spanish - Special Christmas Edition
Photocopiable Games For Teaching Spanish
On Holiday In Spain Cool Kids Speak Spanish
Cool Kids Do Maths In Spanish
Un Extraterrestre En La Tierra
El Mono Que Cambia De Color
Seis Mascotas Maravillosas

The holiday editions have essential words & phrases in part 1. And in part 2 there are challenges to use these words whilst away.

English as a foreign language
Cool Kids Speak English (books 1 & 2)

For more information on the books available, and different ways of learning a foreign language go to https://**learnforeignwords.com**

Made in United States
Orlando, FL
06 February 2022